THE NEW BASIC READERS

CURRICULUM FOUNDATION SERIES

REG. U.S. PAT. OFF.

THE NEW

Days and Deeds

The 1962 Edition

William S. Gray, Marion Monroe,

A. Sterl Artley, May Hill Arbuthnot

SCOTT, FORESMAN AND COMPANY

Chicago Atlanta Dallas Palo Alto Fair Lawn, N. J.

Stories

Young Citizens of Today

Moving Westward

Wonders of Today

Storyland of Here and Now

Young Citizens of Today

Which One?

Dan Drake collected weather vanes. He and Mrs. Drake were unpacking a boxful that he had brought with him to Los Angeles. Dan looked at his mother and sighed.

"What's wrong?" asked Mrs. Drake.

"I don't know what to do with all these vanes," Dan explained. "There's no place to put them here in my new room."

"Maybe Dad can build a shelf," she said.

"There isn't even room for a shelf!" cried Dan. "I've spent lots of time collecting these vanes, and I don't want to store them away. I want them where I can see them."

6

Mrs. Drake smiled. "I know, Dan," she said. "Living in a modern housing project will seem strange for a while. It will be different from living in our large home in Fairfield, Vermont. But maybe we'll like Los Angeles even better than Fairfield."

Dan shook his head doubtfully.

"We'll find a place to put the vanes," his mother told him. "Meanwhile, perhaps you can do an errand for me. I need groceries. Do you know the way to the store?"

"Of course!" Dan declared. "I went there with you yesterday."

"Fine," his mother said. "I need frozen green beans, radishes, a pound of cherries, two alligator pears, whole-wheat bread, flour, eggs, cottage cheese, and soap flakes."

She hesitated as she handed Dan the list and some money. "Now are you *sure* you can find your way back home?" she asked. "Remember that there are many courts here on Marigold Street that look just alike."

"Oh, Mother!" cried Dan. "I'm no baby! I know that our address is 1061 Marigold. How could I get lost?"

Dan left the house and hurried down the court to Marigold Street. Walking along the street, he passed other courts. The houses in each court looked exactly alike. When he came to a vacant lot where some boys were playing ball, he stopped to watch for a while. The boys were yelling happily to one another and did not notice the newcomer.

Suddenly Dan felt very lonely. He missed Tom, his best friend back in Fairfield. "I don't believe I like Los Angeles. A fellow can't have fun without friends," he thought. As he walked on, a lump rose in his throat.

At the store the clerk smiled and talked as he waited on Dan. "Why, he's as nice as the clerks back home," the boy thought.

Feeling less lonely, Dan stepped out of the store into the hot street. At the corner he turned and walked up Marigold. Soon he reached the court that he thought was his.

As Dan was about to enter, he stopped suddenly. The front curtains of the second house on the right were pink. The Drakes' curtains were yellow. Then Dan checked the house number. It was not 1061.

Dan returned to Marigold. All the courts looked just alike. "Which one is mine?" he gasped in dismay. "Have I passed it?"

The boy gave a feeble laugh. "Our house must be farther up the street. I'm sure I'll recognize it," he thought as he walked on.

Finally Dan said to himself, *"This* is our court!" He moved quickly toward the front door of the second house on the right. Then he stopped. In the window was a cardboard sign. *Dachshund Puppies for Sale* it said. Dan did not even own a dog. This could not be his house, but he checked the number just to be sure. Again it was not 1061.

Dan felt very much confused. He was also embarrassed when he saw a boy sitting on the step of the first house. The boy was whistling as he cut away at a piece of wood with a knife. Dan hoped his silly mistake had not been noticed. He hurried toward Marigold Street, pretending not to see the lad. But just as Dan was even with him, the whistling stopped.

"Somebody's lost!" a voice said gleefully.

Because Dan was hot and tired and upset, the teasing tone of the voice annoyed him. Feeling more embarrassed than before, he challenged gruffly, "How do you know?"

The boy looked up. "I just had a hunch," he laughed. "When I first came here, I got lost nearly every day."

Dan said sheepishly, "I can't seem to find the court where I live. My house number is 1061." Then he added shyly, "I'm Dan Drake. I just moved in a few days ago."

"I'm Jay Byrnes," the boy said. He put his knife in his pocket. Then he laid the wood on the step. "Come on. I'll help you find your house," he offered.

As they started up Marigold, Dan asked his new friend, "What were you making?"

"A horse," answered Jay. "I collect toy horses, and sometimes I make them."

When the boys reached Dan's house, Dan showed Jay his horse weather vane. Jay's eyes sparkled. "Boy, that's neat," he said.

Jay looked at the other vanes, too. "I see that no two are alike," he remarked.

"That's right," Dan replied. "Too bad the courts in this housing project aren't as different from one another as the vanes are."

"Hey!" cried Jay. "Why couldn't vanes be used to *make* the courts look different?"

Dan shouted, "That's exactly what I was thinking! And I've been trying to decide what to do with the weather vanes. Let's go see what we can figure out."

Dan handed the horse to Jay. He grabbed a pelican weather vane himself, and the two boys hurried outside. They decided to stick the vanes in the earth. Quickly they planted the pelican vane in front of Dan's house.

Then they went to put the horse weather vane in Jay's yard. Before long, four of the boys who had been playing ball in the lot were standing around, admiring the horse. They began to ask questions. They were eager to see Dan's other weather vanes.

Just then the project manager walked by. "What are you doing, boys?" he inquired pleasantly.

When Dan and Jay told him, he thought for a moment. Then he asked, "Wouldn't weather vanes work better on roofs?"

"Sure!" cried the boys excitedly. "But we didn't suppose it would be allowed."

"Good ideas should always be allowed," the manager chuckled. "I'll send a man with a ladder to help you."

By sundown all the weather vanes were in use. Some were on roof peaks in Dan's court, some in Jay's court, and some in most of the other courts in the project.

13

Dan was outside admiring the vanes when his father came home. Mr. Drake looked puzzled. "Dan, are those your vanes I see scattered all over the project?" he asked.

Dan beamed. "Yes," he said. "Weather vanes really belong out in the wind, so I'm letting my friends use them. We were tired of not being able to find our own houses."

"From the looks of things," Mr. Drake laughed, "you have plenty of friends. We grown-ups got lost, too. But we weren't clever enough to know what to do about it."

"Now everyone can be guided home by the vanes," Dan said happily. "That's the best part. Everyone can enjoy seeing them, too."

Adventure on Lone Gully Trail

Pat and Sally Bower were delighted when Joy and David Swan returned to Lone Gully. The tiny silver-mining camp had been a lonely spot for Sally and Pat while the mine foreman's children were away for a holiday.

This afternoon the four young friends were on the Bowers' porch. David and Joy were telling about a thrilling movie they had seen in the city. "Wild lions and tigers seemed to jump right at you," explained David.

"Say!" cried Sally. "If we had a camera like Uncle Ben's, we could make a movie of the wild animals around here. There are weasels and deer and bears and foxes."

Joy and David were excited by the idea. But Pat just hooted Sally's plan.

Uncle Ben heard Sally's remarks as he came out of the house. "If the four of you want to make a movie," he said, "I'll give you permission to use my camera. It's on my desk, loaded with film and ready to go."

The four youngsters dashed into the house. Pat reached the camera first and grabbed it. "You kids are too young to monkey with a good camera like this," he announced. "I've used it before. So I'll handle it."

"No you won't!" protested Sally violently.

"Now, Sally, remember when you used Grandpa Vernon's fishing outfit?" teased Pat. "You nearly broke the rod in two."

"That was pure accident," Sally muttered.

At that moment Uncle Ben called from the porch, "Pat, I'm riding up to the mine to stay overnight. You're welcome to come along. But you'll have to ride back alone."

"I don't mind," called Pat, moving toward his own room with the camera in his hand. "I'll get my jacket and saddle my horse."

When Clover was saddled, Pat and his uncle started up the mountain trail that led to the Bower mine high above Lone Gully.

Sally glared after Pat. "Just because he's almost fifteen, he needn't act so smart about that camera!" she complained in a waspish tone. "I think I'll get it."

"Pat will be angry if you do," Joy warned.

"Uncle Ben *said* it was for all four of us!" Sally stormed. "But the only time we three will get to use it is when Pat is away."

Just then Mr. Bower and Mr. Swan came down the trail. Mr. Bower was saying to the mine foreman, "It must have been a big bear."

"Hi, Dad!" Sally called out. "Did you see a bear on the trail?"

"No," said Mr. Bower. "Just some fresh claw marks on a tree trunk."

The men rode off to the stable, and Sally turned to David. "Wouldn't it be splendid if we could get a moving picture of that bear?"

"Wow! Let's try," said David excitedly.

Sally ran to Pat's room and turned the door handle. "It's locked!" she wailed.

"I'll go in through a window," David said.

Five minutes later the children had the camera and were starting up the mountain.

They climbed for half an hour. Then the trail grew rockier and steeper. Joy puffed, "I'm tired! My feet hurt! Let's go home."

David panted, "I wish we knew how far up the trail those claw marks are."

"Hope it isn't much farther," Sally gasped. "Let's sit here on a log for a few minutes."

After a short rest, they tramped off again. Suddenly from up the narrow trail came the terrified whinny of a horse.

"Maybe our bear scared the horse," Sally whispered. She raised the camera and held it securely, prepared to take pictures.

Then a mare came charging madly down the trail. It was Clover. Her mane was flying, and Pat was clinging to her back.

18

"Bear! Bear!" yelled Pat.

Joy shrieked and grabbed David's arm. But Sally did not budge. She kept the camera aimed at Clover as the mare swept by.

Joy shrieked again as an enormous beast with tar-black fur lunged into view.

As Joy's second cry pierced the air, the bear stopped in its tracks. Its cruel-looking eyes glared at the children threateningly.

"Yell louder!" Sally commanded.

Immediately Joy let out a deafening shriek, and David added an ear-smashing howl.

After regarding the children fiercely for a second, the startled bear stepped from the trail and lumbered away into the forest.

Sally lowered the camera with trembling hands. "Boy! Was I scared!" she squeaked.

"Please, can't we go home?" Joy pleaded.

"We'll go as fast as we can," Sally told her. "I'm anxious to see about Pat."

"I hope you got a good picture of that old bear," David remarked as they scampered down the trail. "Do you think you did?"

"Yes," said Sally breathlessly. "What I hope is that I got a good picture of Pat. I think he was scared worse than we were."

When the children met Pat riding up the trail, Sally whisked the camera behind her.

"I'm glad you're all right," Pat said with relief. "I came back as soon as I could. Clover reared, and I couldn't hold her when she saw that bear. Did it try to hurt you?"

"No. It was an old fraidy cat!" boasted Joy. "We just yelled, and it ran off."

When they got home, Pat rode Clover to the stable. In the house, Sally took the film out and put the camera back in Pat's room.

"When our film is developed, we shall surprise Pat," she told David and Joy.

Twelve days later the developed film was back. That evening Sally asked Joy and David to come over. Soon after they arrived, Sally winked at them and said to her brother, "Let's have a movie, Pat."

"Sure," said Pat. "I'll show our trout fishing trip." He laid the film by the movie machine and went to put up the screen.

Sally quickly concealed *his* film under a newspaper and laid *her* film by the machine.

Soon the movie began. But it did not show the events of the family fishing trip.

"What's this?" Pat cried when a runaway steed and its rider flashed on the screen.

Joy and Sally giggled mischievously.

Pat studied the screen intently. When a bear appeared, he turned off the machine.

"Recognize anybody?" Sally inquired.

"I recognize me," replied Pat sheepishly. "And I know who took the picture."

Sally flipped on the ceiling light. "You'll have to admit it's a good movie," she said.

"Pure accident!" Pat declared gruffly.

Sally snatched up a cushion from a chair and flung it playfully at Pat. He caught the cushion in the air. "Anyway," he remarked, grinning around the pillow at his sister, "I'm proud of you, Sally. From now on we'll take turns using the camera."

The Echo Mystery

Ricky Knight poured sand out of his boots and wiped his damp forehead. He and two friends had been exploring sandy canyons, caves, and rock ledges since morning. Now it was almost noon, and he had not seen his companions, Don and George, for an hour.

"Hey, Don!" Ricky called loudly.

Hey, Don! replied a deep, hoarse echo.

"That's queer," Ricky said to himself. "We fellows have been here dozens of times. And I never heard an echo before."

Ricky called out again, "Hey, Don!"

The words echoed back mournfully.

Just then an amused voice above Ricky asked, "What's all the yelling about?"

Ricky glanced quickly upward. He saw
Don Mills poking his grinning face around
some mesquite bushes on a ledge higher up.
George Thornton was beside him.

"Well, hi!" cried Ricky. "I just heard an
odd echo. It came from Red Man's Cave."

"The heat's got you!" hooted Don. "We've
spent hours prowling around here recently.
And we have never once heard an echo."

"I did," Ricky insisted. "Just now."

"Prove it, chum," Don challenged.

"Come down, and I will," replied Ricky.

Don and George promptly slid down. Then Ricky stood up and called, "Hey, Don!"

The call came echoing back hoarsely.

Don yelled, "Ho, Ricky!" But no distant echo replied. There was complete silence.

"You're probably not standing in just the right place," Ricky suggested. He called Don's name again, and the echo answered.

"That's proof," Don admitted. "But I don't understand why we've never heard it before. Now let's eat before we starve to death."

The boys talked about the freak echo while they cooked and ate lunch. As they were strolling home, Don cried, "Hey! I can use that echo to tease my stuck-up sister June. She always says 'How boring!' when I try to tell her about our caves. But she loves mysteries. I'll tell her we heard the spook of a dead Indian in Red Man's Cave."

"She ought to hear it," Ricky cackled.

Just then George had an idea. "My folks are having company tomorrow!" he cried. "There'll be a couple of girl cousins that I'll have to entertain. Let's invite them and June out here for a picnic."

June Mills and George's guests, Martha Frost and Kitty Grogan, accepted the picnic invitation with pleasure. Ricky told his little sister Bunny Jean that she could tag along, too, and she was wildly excited.

On the way to the picnic the boys talked mysteriously about the spook. When the group reached the stone ledge where Ricky had heard the curious echo the day before, the boys halted. Then Don strutted to the exact spot where Ricky had stood.

"Why stop here?" June demanded. "You said the spook was in Red Man's Cave."

"Hush, everyone," Ricky said. "We'll call to the spook. He'll answer from the cave."

Then in an extra loud voice Don shouted confidently, "Hey, Red Man!"

There was no answering call.

Muttering to himself, Don moved a few steps to the right. "Hey, Red Man!" he yelled and cupped a hand around his ear.

Not a sound came back.

Don moved several steps to the left and screamed desperately, "Hey, Red Man!"

Still there was no echo.

The boys were puzzled and embarrassed. They looked helplessly at one another.

Kitty, Martha, and Bunny shrieked with laughter. June stood with her arms folded and jeered, "Where is your spook?"

Don confessed uncomfortably, "I don't know. We heard a scary echo right here yesterday. Honest, we did. We decided it came from Red Man's Cave."

All three boys admitted that the joke had backfired. They took the girls' laughing and teasing good-naturedly.

Even though the spook had been a great disappointment, the youngsters had fun cooking and eating a delicious meal.

While the others were packing up, Ricky climbed up on the ledge to look around.

"Hey, Don!" he yelled. He was going to continue, "Come on up here." But to his amazement the call *Hey, Don!* came drifting back from the distance.

"What was that?" Martha exclaimed.

"O-o-h, m-my!" stuttered June. "It must be the echo from Red Man's Cave. I can't imagine why we didn't hear it before."

Twice more Ricky repeated the call from different spots on the ledge. Each time, the croaking echo answered. Then as the group stood puzzled and silent, the call *Hey, Don!* came again from the direction of the cave.

"It's a person calling!" June cried. "Let's go find him. Come on, everyone!"

The boys and girls grabbed the big picnic baskets and ran. At Red Man's Cave they spent a long time searching, but they found no one. Finally, hot and tired, they gave up the unsuccessful man hunt and started home.

"I'm thirsty," said Ricky. "Let's stop and ask Mr. Lowell for a drink of water. His hut is right behind that ridge."

When they got to the hut, Mr. Lowell told them to help themselves. The old gentleman stood and talked while the youngsters, one by one, got a cold drink from the bubbly spring and started down the trail.

Ricky drank last. "Thanks, Mr. Lowell," he said. Just then he noticed that Don had left his picnic basket beside the spring.

"Hey, Don! Your picnic stuff!" he called. *Hey, Don!* came an answer from nearby.

Ricky wheeled about. "That cry, sir!" he exclaimed. *"Who* is it? Or *what* is it?"

Before the man could reply, the other two boys and the four girls came racing back.

"That's Albert," Mr. Lowell was saying.

"I don't know Albert," George said. "But he must be the spook that called to us."

The three boys all talked at once, telling about the spooky echo they had heard.

Mr. Lowell laughingly assured the boys, "Albert is the spook." Then motioning the others to follow, he started around the hut.

In a cage behind the hut sat a parrot with brilliantly colored feathers. "Hello, Don!" he squawked to each child in turn.

"Why does the parrot call each one of us Don?" Bunny asked.

Mr. Lowell replied, "That's the only name he knows. He belongs to my nephew, Don, who is away on a trip. Don brought Albert to stay with me, and the parrot is lonely."

"Poor bird," murmured Bunny. "Maybe he heard Ricky calling Don and thought his master was home again. Poor Albert."

When the seven youngsters left for home, they each passed the parrot's wire cage and called out, "Good-by, Albert." And for seven times without stopping, the bird croaked, "Good-by, Don!"

Red Flame

Jim Barber, in his new cowboy vest and hat, sat astride the fence. "Hi, Solomon!" he called to the horse standing nearby.

The horse lifted his head and eyed the boy.

"If only I had a horse like Solomon," Jim sighed, "I could be a real cowboy."

Jim loved horses, and so he was delighted when he and his mother had come recently to live with Aunt Ellen at the Circle F ranch.

Solomon belonged on the next ranch, the Double V. Just why he stood alone in the pasture day after day, Jim did not know. But he did know that the horse looked very wise. That was the reason Jim called him Solomon.

Today young Jim Barber gazed longingly at Solomon. He had a very special reason for doing so. The yearly rodeo at Deadwater was now only a week away. Jim longed to ride with the daring cowboys of the Circle F ranch. And this year the rodeo was open to boy riders.

"Hi, Solomon!" Jim called out again. This time the horse came toward the fence with a friendly whinny and began nuzzling him for a carrot. When Jim had first seen Solomon, the horse had acted very unfriendly. Since then Jim had given him carrots and lumps of sugar. And now they were friends.

From the top of the fence, Jim flung himself up on the horse's back, as he had done many times before. Solomon tossed his head and galloped off joyfully. Hearing the clatter of hoofs beneath him gave Jim a thrill.

"I can ride a horse, anyway," he thought, "even if I don't own one."

Soon Solomon stopped. Jim got down and gave him a carrot. For a moment he gently rubbed the horse's nose. Then he headed back toward the Circle F.

After supper Jim sat on the ranch-house porch with the cowboys. He listened to them as they talked about the rodeo.

"Timson of the Double V is making his old offer again this year," said Frank Hawk, the foreman. "He says anyone who can ride that Red Flame of his can have him."

The Circle F cowboys had all tried their luck with Red Flame. He was a challenge to their fame as riders. But no one had yet been able to stay on Timson's red horse.

After the men went to the bunkhouse, Jim sat looking off toward the far hills. He was wondering if the foreman or one of the cowboys would take him to the rodeo.

The first day of the great yearly celebration finally came. At dawn cowboys in their best outfits began to ride by the Circle F toward Deadwater. Jim was excited indeed, but he still did not know if the foreman planned to take him along.

Soon Frank Hawk hailed him, "Come on, cowboy, if you're going to Deadwater!"

Hastily calling good-by to his mother, Jim shot from the house like a streak.

When Jim and Frank arrived in Deadwater, Jim was thrilled to find the streets crowded with horses and real cowboys.

"There will be some greenhorns here who will try to ride Red Flame," Frank chuckled. "Want to see them?"

"Oh, yes!" Jim exclaimed. He was eager to see that dangerous animal, Red Flame.

"Come along then," said Frank. "We'll try to get a good place at the corral fence. But it won't be easy. Lots of folks will want to see if anyone can ride Red Flame."

One by one the events of the rodeo took place. Then came the most exciting one of all. The old offer was made. Red Flame would be given to any rider who could stay on his back for eight seconds.

The watchers pressed closer to the fence. Suddenly a gate opened, and Red Flame shot out into view. The horse reared and bucked under the unwelcome load on his back. A few seconds later Jim saw a hat go sailing to the ground, followed by its owner.

Jim watched Red Flame as he burst out of the gate four times. Each rider was thrown headlong. Each got up and limped away.

The gate burst open for the fifth time, and Red Flame came bounding out. The fifth man did no better than the others. Off he went like all the rest.

This time Red Flame did not plunge to the far end of the corral as he had done before. He galloped over to the fence where Jim and Frank Hawk were sitting.

In a flash Jim reached out for the horse's mane and was on Red Flame's back.

"Stop that boy. He'll be killed!" the owner of the horse yelled.

A fearful hush fell on the watchers. They were sure Jim would be injured. But instead the horse galloped steadily and proudly about the corral. In a few minutes Jim dismounted amid wild cheers from the audience.

Red Flame's worried owner soon emerged from the crowd. "Lad!" he exclaimed. "I don't know how you could ride that horse, but you did. And he's yours. Pick him up at the entrance and take him home with you."

When Jim rode into the yard that evening, his mother was on the porch. "*Where* did you get that beautiful horse?" she cried.

"I won him by riding him," Jim replied.

"That's wonderful!" Mrs. Barber gasped in amazement. "What's—what's his name?"

"His owner named him Red Flame, but I call him Solomon—a name he earned today."

The Swinging Bridge

"Mother, isn't it perfect!" cried Frannie. "I've lived in Brookside for only a few weeks. But I'm in a Scout troop already, and I'm going to camp for the very first time. The bus will stop for me any minute now." Then an anxious look crept into Frannie's eyes. "I hope I won't be 'Fraidy Frannie' at camp. Sometimes I can't help being afraid."

"I know," Mrs. Colt said. "Just remember there's usually no reason to be afraid."

"I hate water," Frannie declared. "But Mrs. Wolf says spring vacation is much too early for swimming. I'm sure I can be as brave as a lion about anything else. Oh, I do want my new friends to like me."

Just at noon sixteen Scouts and Mrs. Wolf, their leader, reached Crystal Lake Camp.

Old Mr. Deal, the caretaker of the camp, was away for a few days. His plump, jolly wife had a steaming pot of chicken stew with rice and mushrooms, hot rolls and crab apple butter, and chocolate pie ready for the girls.

They spent the afternoon getting settled in double cabins and playing games beside the lake. After supper they made taffy candy and sang songs before a crackling fire.

As Frannie was falling asleep that night, she thought, "What a goose I was to worry! There isn't a single scary thing about camp."

The next morning Mrs. Wolf said, "It's a lovely day, girls. By tomorrow those clouds around Bear Mountain may bring rain. We'd better hike to the falls today."

"Goody!" cried half a dozen Scouts.

"That hike is our favorite," Rose Taylor told Frannie. "You'll like it, too."

Frannie did like the first part of the hike. The girls skipped through the woods along a well-marked trail. They stopped often to look at wild flowers or to listen to a bird.

Once from a very high cliff Rose Taylor pointed out a creek. "That's Bear Creek," she said.

It was dashing noisily downhill, splashing itself against rocks in the creek bed.

The tumbling water looked wild and awful to Frannie, who was not yet used to mountain streams. She forgot it, though, until the path curved downward all at once and then led to a swinging footbridge over the creek.

"First one over!" yelled Jane Carpenter as her feet made the bridge swing and dance.

Frannie saw, in the depths below, swiftly flowing water that churned and boiled into a soapsudsy foam. Her face turned pale, and she shuddered.

Poor frightened Frannie appealed to Rose Taylor. "Isn't there—some—other way?" she stammered. "To the falls, I mean?"

Rose said, "Not unless we drive ten miles around the highway and then hike two miles."

One by one, thirteen more Scouts raced past Frannie and crossed the bridge. Then both Mrs. Wolf and Rose grasped Frannie's hands. The terrified girl took one shaky step forward and stopped.

Shrinking from the bridge, she sobbed, "I can't! I can't cross this bouncy bridge."

Rose coaxed her to try it. But Frannie did not have the courage. She heard Jane chanting, "Fraidy cat! Fraidy Frannie!"

Then Rose offered to accompany Frannie back to camp. But Frannie said she would rather go alone. Mrs. Wolf agreed that she could follow the marked trail by herself.

When Frannie entered the camp kitchen, Auntie Deal was sliding a pan of nut cookies into the oven to bake. "So you didn't like the swinging bridge," the plump old lady said.

"No, it made me dizzy," Frannie replied, heaving a sigh. "But how did you know?"

"Lots of girls don't like it at first," Mrs. Deal chuckled. She pushed a bowl and a big spoon toward Frannie. "This cookie bowl is ready for scraping, and we'll turn on the radio. There's a good program on now."

Frannie listened to the radio and scraped at the cookie bowl. Suddenly an announcer interrupted the program. He said that there had been a big cloudburst on Bear Mountain. Flood water was rushing down Bear Creek. In two hours it would reach Claypool, just a mile above Crystal Lake.

"Gracious, that's bad!" clucked Mrs. Deal. "The creek's high already from melted snow and all the rain we've had recently. I wish the folks hadn't gone to the falls today."

Frannie asked weakly, "Will they drown?"

"They'll be safe," Mrs. Deal said as she untied her apron. "But the swinging bridge may wash away. They'll be trapped on the far side of the creek tonight. I should go to warn them. But, no, I'm slow as a turtle. The flood would get there before I did."

Frannie shivered at the idea of spending a night out in the mountains. She wondered if the other girls would be scared. She *could* go to warn them about the flood—if it were not for that awful bridge. She had plenty of time, and the trail was marked.

"I'll go," she said in a determined voice.

Along the path through the timber Frannie raced. At the ridge where the trail curved down to the creek, she glanced quickly at the swirling water. It was not rising yet.

Frannie took a deep breath and sped to the bridge. Her feet skimmed across it.

The trail climbed steeply on the other side of the creek, and Frannie had to slow down. She thought she would *never* reach the falls. She could hear them—a low roar that grew louder and louder. Then at last she burst through an opening in the trees.

There were the thundering falls! There were the girls, laying wood on some rocks for a campfire. They called out in surprise when they saw Frannie.

"There's a cloudburst on Bear Mountain!" panted Frannie. "The radio says a flood is coming. If the bridge washes away, you'll be trapped."

Mrs. Wolf and all the girls scurried about, gathering up jackets, sweaters, hats, and the picnic things. Then the leader, followed by Frannie and the other Scouts, set off down the trail toward Crystal Lake Camp.

At Bear Creek, Mrs. Wolf stepped to one side, motioning for the girl behind her to take the lead. It was Frannie. Confidently she strode across the bridge, and fifteen Scouts soon followed. On the other side the girls all stopped to wait for Mrs. Wolf.

"Goodness, but you're brave!" Jane said to Frannie admiringly. "Weren't you scared stiff to cross that bridge all alone with a flood coming? I'm sorry I called you a fraidy cat. You're not. You're brave as a lion!"

The Silver Penny

For the tenth time that forenoon Howard Gordon rode his bicycle slowly around the square. Behind the gaily decorated bicycle rolled a coaster wagon. Mounted firmly on the wagon was a huge sign.

Howard wanted to attract attention. And he was succeeding very well. When people on the street caught a glimpse of this brief parade, they stopped and stared. When they read the lettering on the sign, they burst out laughing.

A picture of a fat man decorated the sign. Above and beside him in large eye-catching letters appeared these words:

See world's most amazing magician!
Anybody 300 pounds or over admitted free!
All others ten cents.
Saturday at 2 o'clock. Skinners' yard.
Benefit of Red Cross.
Buy tickets today!

As Howard rode slowly around a corner, a boy on a green bike flashed up beside him.

"Hey, slowpoke, how about a race?" the boy challenged.

"Can't today, Jason," Howard answered. "I'm advertising the greatest magic show on earth. Ted and I are putting it on. It's a benefit to earn money for the Red Cross."

"Who's going to be the amazing magician? You?" hooted Jason Hatch.

"Ted is. I'm his assistant," replied Howard.

Jason snorted. Then he asked, "What kind of magic can Ted Skinner do?"

"Read the fine print and see," said Howard.

Jason dropped back and studied the small lettering at the bottom of the sign.

Jason squinted as he read, "See magician produce live rabbit from hat. Make quarter disappear. Change copper penny to silver."

"I'll take a ticket," he said, giving a dime to Howard. "I'll be at the show, and you'd better make good on all those promises."

As Jason rode off, Howard realized that he was hungry. He had been working hard since ten o'clock. He knew that Ted had been at work, too, practicing his magic stunts. Howard was going around after lunch to see how Ted was getting along.

Ted was practicing some coin tricks when Howard arrived. He put a shiny new quarter between his hands and squeezed it. When he opened his hands again, the coin was gone. Quickly he reached up and seemed to grab the quarter right out of the air.

"Neat!" exclaimed Howard. "I didn't see a thing!"

Ted nodded with satisfaction. "If I'm able to fool you, I can fool anybody," he boasted.

Howard said anxiously, "Jason is coming to the benefit. I'm sorry I sold him a ticket. I'm afraid he means mischief."

"Maybe," Ted agreed. "He still suspects that we put his bicycle up on the flagpole last Halloween. He'll probably do something at the show to get even."

Ted chuckled and then added, "If we hadn't seen his old bike, he'd be looking for it yet. His dad had the police searching for it, but they didn't think to look up in the air."

"Well, Jason mentioned something about our making good," Howard said. "If you fail on any of the tricks, he may cause trouble."

"I won't fail," Ted promised.

On Saturday Jason and his chums arrived early. Howard and Ted were selling tickets.

At show time the two boys dashed into the dressing tent. Howard hastily glanced over the articles required for the magic tricks.

"I saw Jason go in here," he explained. "But I guess he didn't bother anything."

Soon he and Ted stepped out on the stage.

Immediately Jason got up from his bench. He yelled out, "Unless you two do absolutely everything you advertised, we'll demand our money back. Am I right, fellows?"

"Yes," yelled several of Jason's friends.

"We'll make good," Howard stated firmly. "Now may I introduce Professor Skinner. He will astonish you with feats of magic."

Ted quickly pushed up his sleeves. Then he poured water into a glass. He breathed on the water, and it changed to a rosy red color. When he passed his hand over the glass, the red changed to deep blue. Then he spread a handkerchief over the glass and mumbled a few words. He whisked off the handkerchief, and the water was clear.

During the program Ted got applause from everyone except Jason and his crowd. They just sat. They did not clap once.

Finally Ted came to the very last act. He asked someone in the audience to lend him a penny. Almost before the words were out of his mouth, Jason offered a coin.

"Do you mind if I change this copper penny to silver?" Ted asked politely.

"No, Professor," answered Jason. "Go right ahead with your feat of magic."

At that instant Howard stepped out on the stage. Under his breath he gasped, "The jar of stuff is gone! I've hunted all over. Jason must have sneaked in and taken it."

Both boys glanced at Jason. They saw that he was grinning broadly.

Howard whispered, "Try a mind-reading act. I'll try to get more—" His voice grew fainter as he entered the tent.

Looking straight at Jason, Ted said slowly, "There seem to be some unfriendly spirits about. While my magic power drives them away, I'll do some mind reading. Then I'll change the copper penny to silver. Who'll ask a question to start the act?"

"I will!" Jason shouted harshly. "Who put my bike on the flagpole?"

Ted waved a hand over the audience while he was wondering what to do next. He happened to point at Sam Robinson, a friend of Jason's. Sam's face got red. Suddenly he got up and hurried away. Everyone knew at once that he was the guilty person.

Another boy wanted to ask a question. But Ted heard a sound of glass breaking inside the tent. Then Howard emerged.

Instantly Ted saw a silvery gleam in the white cloth that Howard was carrying. Tossing Jason's penny to him, Ted said, "Note the date so you'll recognize the coin later."

Jason returned the penny, and Ted quickly placed it in the cloth. He rubbed his hands together and spoke some magic words. Then Ted removed the cloth and displayed a shiny silver coin. "Is this your penny?" he asked as he threw the coin to Jason.

Surprised and laughing, Jason nodded. The audience burst into wild applause.

After the show Jason lingered until everyone else had gone. Pulling a jar from his pocket, he said, "I took the mercury, Ted, so that you couldn't coat a penny with it." Then as Jason dashed off, he yelled, "You're really good! I'm glad to know who hid my bike."

Ted said, "Now then, my worthy assistant, explain how you got that mercury so fast."

Howard dodged into the tent and returned carrying a paper with a thermometer on it.

"You're the magician," he said. "Can you change this broken thermometer into a good one before your mother finds out it's gone?"

"Simple," laughed Ted. "Just give me a dollar and five minutes' time. I'll produce a thermometer—from the drugstore!"

Weight for Daniel

As Jack Moss unloaded his big hog at an Indiana stock show, he sighed with relief.

Getting Daniel to the county show had been a problem. First there had been difficulty in arranging for a truck to haul the hog. Then the trip itself had been long and rainy. But now surely Jack's troubles were over.

"Think you can win anything with one old hog?" Jack heard a voice ask. He looked up and saw Art Price, a boy from home. He was guarding a red steer and a white hog.

Jack asked earnestly, "What do you think? You've been to junior contests before."

"I always exhibit at least two animals," Art said with a laugh. "You have only one, and he doesn't look so good to me."

As Jack watched Art and his fine animals enter a building, he decided that Daniel was not very handsome. Riding in a dirty truck in the rain had not improved his appearance.

Jack and his muddy hog slowly followed Art. Inside the crowded show building were the scales. Jack stopped to watch some boys weighing their animals. A friendly older lad politely introduced himself as Paul Meadows and offered to weigh Daniel. "Of course," he said, "a judge weighs him for the contest."

Paul weighed Daniel. "What a shame!" he said to Jack. "He's tipping the scales at 302 pounds. Two pounds too much for the class in which he'll be shown."

"All the time I was afraid that I wouldn't have my hog fat enough," Jack related sadly. "Maybe I should load him up and go home."

Paul remarked jokingly, "There are two pounds of mud on him. Clean him up. His weight may be different by judging time."

"You're right!" cried Jack. "I can't give up now. Where can I get a pail of water?"

Paul explained kindly, "You don't want a pail. Use the hose outside. Curry him with this." Paul gave Jack a steel-toothed brush. Then he added, "I'll help you."

Jack was extremely glad to have help. It took one boy to hold the hog while the other boy scrubbed. Daniel hated the currying, but it worked wonders on his mud-caked hair. Soon his skin glowed, and his hair shone.

"Say!" exclaimed Paul. "He's a *beauty!*"

Feeling a little ashamed, Jack drawled, "I guess it's evident that this is my first show. I'm a greenhorn, all right, or I would have spruced Daniel up before anybody saw him."

"I've attended several stock shows," said Paul, "and I still have plenty to learn. I've had the help of a fine 4-H leader, too."

Both boys stood back and studied Daniel.

"He *is* handsome," Jack said with pride. "If only he weighed just a little bit less."

"Yes," Paul agreed. "Then he'd surely have a chance to win."

Just then Daniel, stirred up by the washing and currying and the noisy throngs of boys, took flight. He dived into a doorway and then raced along an aisle between rows of pens.

Jack and Paul ran down the alleyway after Daniel. But they were not able to catch him. The frisky hog had more tricks than a circus. Each time the boys thought they had him, he spun around and ran the opposite way.

Suddenly a loud voice announced the cattle contest in which Paul had entered a steer.

"Go on, Paul," Jack urged. "I can catch Daniel alone. I hope you win a ribbon."

By now the hog was some distance away. He was trotting past a group of older boys who were admiring his satiny sides.

"Catch him!" shouted Jack.

The boys were fast, but Daniel was faster. He made a sudden detour around some baled straw and a pile of fodder and got away.

Several boys pursued the fleeing hog. But the more they chased, the faster Daniel ran. Finally he bolted down a different alleyway. Then, panting and laughing, the other boys stopped. And Jack sped after Daniel alone.

"That hog of mine!" he grumbled. "He's more trouble than a whole litter of pigs. He's asking to be made into bacon grease."

Daniel was tiring, however. Jack thought he might capture him in a few more steps.

"Hi, pork chops!" called a boy as Daniel ambled by. He slapped the hog with a switch. Off Daniel ran just as Jack grabbed for him. Down went Jack, sprawling at Daniel's heels.

Suddenly Jack heard a voice announce the junior contest in which Daniel was entered. "Weigh in. Weigh in. Line up for judging in pen number eight," the voice over the loud-speaker continued.

Jack began calling to Daniel. "Woo—eee! Woo—ee! Woo—ee!" he coaxed in his best come-to-dinner voice. But he coaxed in vain. Daniel did not heed the calls.

With aching legs Jack ran on. He wished he had never *seen* a hog. This crazy chase might go on until midnight. Just then a gate blocking the alleyway between pens closed ahead of Daniel. He was a prisoner at last!

In a few minutes Jack led his weary hog up to pen number eight. One of the judges waved Jack and Daniel into the judging pen.

"My hog's not weighed!" Jack insisted.

"Do it later if he places," said the judge.

Jack saw dozens of boys and hogs standing in a long line in the center of the pen. He stepped quickly into line beside Art Price.

Art paid no attention to Jack and Daniel. He was far too busy trying to force his own handsome hog to stand still.

The judges worked slowly down the line, studying each hog. On the second trip the gentlemen motioned some boys to the far end. That was the place for winners. Jack saw Art's fine hog moved into first place.

Then, for the third time, the judges started along the line of hogs. When they came to Daniel, one judge paused. He felt Daniel's firm sides and studied him from the back.

"Take him up to second place," he said.

Jack's heart beat rapidly as he guided his hog forward.

Again Jack stood beside Art Price and his nervous hog. Jack lost count of the number of times the judges compared one hog with another and shuffled and reshuffled the line.

"You, there! Move to first place," a judge shouted to Jack. Throughout the remaining reshufflings, Jack and Daniel stayed in that prized spot.

The judges were about to hand Jack the blue ribbon when Art Price spoke. "It's not fair!" he cried. "That hog wasn't weighed in. And I happen to know that he was two pounds heavy this morning."

"That's right," Jack admitted. "I was late, and a judge said to weigh afterwards."

The judges decided that Jack had intended nothing wrong. The hog should be weighed. If Daniel weighed less than three hundred pounds, the ribbon was his. If he weighed more, he was out of the contest.

A crowd gathered near the scales. Daniel stood motionless as if he realized that this was his big moment. Jack hardly breathed.

Slowly the hog weigher proclaimed, "Two hundred ninety-nine and three-quarters."

Jack's worries vanished like the air from a popped balloon. He sighed as the bright blue ribbon was put into his outstretched hand.

A boy nearby was talking to Art Price.

Jack heard him say, "Sure! I saw him running his hog. He's smart and deserved to win. He knew how to take down the hog's weight. He reduced him by running him."

"I reduced him all right," Jack said with a grin. "I reduced *both* of us. But I don't believe Daniel won just because he was the correct weight. The reason he won was that he behaved himself and stood still. After that gallop he was too tired to do anything else."

A New Star

One spring day Josie and Joe Dawn burst into their house. Josie was almost in tears.

"Joe won't let me play ball with his team when they're practicing," she wailed.

"A-w, Mother!" cried Joe, who *was* fond of his twin. "My friends all like Josie. She plays fine. But when there's a whole crowd of boys and only one girl, it makes a fellow feel funny if the girl is his sister."

Here was Josie's problem again. She was just a girl. She looked like her twin brother. She was happiest wearing clothes like Joe's and playing the games Joe played. But still she was just a girl.

Mrs. Dawn realized how both children felt. "Joe is right, dear," she said. "You may play when a few of the boys practice batting. But when the entire fifth-grade team plays, you must be a good sport and come home."

"Then I'll have a girls' team!" Josie said. But she soon found that her friends preferred girls' games. Josie did manage to play ball, though. She persuaded her dad to pitch for her occasionally. She had some opportunities to play when Joe's chums needed a player.

Josie was a good batter. The boys teased, but Josie did not mind. "Watch Josie!" they joked. "If she hits the ball, you may have to run all the way to China to get it."

In the month of May the Lowell fifth-grade team began to play other schools. How Josie wished she could play! She was sure she could bat the ball beyond China if necessary.

Joe's team won game after game. Finally they had only to beat the Whittier fifth grade to become the city champions. Since Josie could not play with the team, she insisted that Joe practice every evening after supper. He must play well enough for both of them.

At last the day before the great Lowell-Whittier match came. The game was set for nine-thirty Saturday morning.

Joe's team practiced Friday after school. Joe did not get home until almost six o'clock. Then he just sat hunched up in a big chair.

"Don't want any dinner. I'm not hungry," he said when Josie called him to the table.

"What's the matter?" she asked in alarm.

"Nothing," growled Joe. "I'm chilly and tired. Can't a fellow lose his appetite without your thinking something's the matter?"

Although Joe kept protesting that he was all right, his mother took his temperature and sent him to bed early.

When Joe woke on Saturday, he admitted that he was too ill to play ball. "What luck," he moaned. "The team *needs* me today."

"What dreadful luck!" his twin groaned in despair. "Oh, Joe, I'm so sorry. Can I do anything for you?"

"Yes," he replied. "Let the captain know that I can't be there. Then go cheer just as loud as you can. The boys always say that your cheering helps as much as my playing. And remember all the plays so that you can tell me about them."

Mr. and Mrs. Dawn agreed with Joe that Josie should see the game. "But you must go to the barber shop first," Mrs. Dawn said. "You can't attend Jill Grant's birthday party this afternoon unless your hair is trimmed. Tony knows the way it should be."

"All right, Mother," sighed Josie. "I'll go straight to the shop and then on to the game. Oh, Joe, I wish you could play! But I'll tell you every single thing that happens."

A block from home Josie met Bob Gray, the captain of the Lowell team. "Hi, Josie," he said in a worried tone. "Have you heard about Bill Fleetwood? He hurt his knee and can't play. Don't know whether we can win without him or not. He and Joe are our best hitters. Good thing we still have Joe."

Josie started to give Joe's message to Bob. But something stopped her. She had an idea.

"You don't need to go by for Joe," she said. "He can't leave for a while." Then, fearing she would be questioned further about her brother, she ran like the wind.

Josie argued with herself all the way to the barber shop. Once in the big leather chair, however, she made up her mind.

"Cut my hair *real* short, Tony," she said.

Tony eyed his customer doubtfully. "Your mother generally likes your hair a little bit longer," he said.

"She won't care if it's short this time, I'm sure!" Josie answered. Then she thought, "Not when she knows why I did it."

When Tony had finished, Josie looked at her reflection in the mirror. "Oh!" she cried. "Now I look more like Joe than ever!"

Josie ran home like lightning. It was easy for her to steal down the basement stairs and into the closet where the twins' skates, sled, and play clothes were kept. Quickly she put on Joe's baseball suit and shoes. Then she arranged his cap on her new haircut.

Just three minutes before game time Josie boldly ran onto the ball diamond. When the members of the Lowell team saw her, they stamped their feet and chanted,

"Here's Joe! Joe! Joe!
Now we'll go! Go! Go!"

Josie thrilled with excitement. "I *must* hit that ball hard," she thought. "I must make it go all the way to China for Joe and the other boys. They must be the champions."

The umpire shouted, "Play ball!" When Josie came up to bat for Lowell in the first inning, she was so excited that she fanned.

"What's wrong, Joe?" inquired Bob Gray. "Forgotten how to bat?"

Josie soon settled down. In later innings she got two hits.

Throughout the game, the score kept going up and down like a seesaw. First Whittier was ahead, then Lowell. The score stood 15 to 14 in the last inning, with Whittier leading. Two of the Lowell batters were out. Three runners were on base. Josie was up at bat.

"It's up to me now," muttered scared little Josie. "I *must not* lose this game."

She grasped the bat with shaking hands. The ball whizzed toward her. Josie swung furiously—and missed.

Several spectators groaned.

"Strike one," called the umpire.

As if in a dream, Josie heard the umpire announce, one after another, "Ball one. Ball two. Strike two. Ball three."

"I've only one more chance," thought Josie. For the last time, she swung the bat.

There was a loud crack! The ball soared into the sky.

Josie's feet skimmed over the ground.

First base! As Josie ran on to second, she saw a runner cross home plate. The score was even, 15 to 15.

The ball had landed in a patch of weeds. Fielders were hunting frantically for it.

Second base! Now another runner scored. The game was won, but Josie did not stop.

Third base! Josie reached it just as the runner ahead of her slid home.

Then Josie saw a Whittier fielder pick up the ball and throw it. "Run! Beat the ball! Go it, Joe!" cried the spectators.

Josie flew. The ball flew, too, straight into the outstretched hands of the excited Whittier catcher. But he dropped the ball! Josie slid to home plate—safe—and lay there panting.

"Good old Joe! Good old Joe!

He made things go! He made things go!" chanted the Lowell boys in frenzied joy.

Mr. Dawn happened to be walking past the ball field at that moment. He dashed over to see what was causing the uproar.

Half a dozen eager voices greeted him.

"You ought to have seen Joe! Good old Joe! He won the game. He hit a home run. With the bases loaded! Good for Joe!"

"Joe made a home run?" asked Mr. Dawn in astonishment.

Hurriedly he pushed his way through the crowd to home plate. His eyes lighted on a panting and red-faced little ball player, who was grinning at him sheepishly.

Although the twins looked very much alike, their father could always tell the two apart. Josie had dimples that appeared in her cheeks whenever she was embarrassed. Her dimples were showing now.

"Sorry, fellows!" said Mr. Dawn. "This isn't Joe. It's Josie! Joe's home in bed."

Josie had recovered enough breath to talk. "Oh, Daddy! I wanted the team to win. I can play *almost* as well as Joe. When he couldn't come, I decided to take his place and not let anybody know."

"Oh, Josie!" was all her father could say.

The Lowell team yelled and cheered. Even the Whittier boys joined in.

"Josie! Josie! Best by far!
Here's to Lowell's new baseball star!"

The Big Word

Robert Beacham sat with his eyes closed so that he could not see the dictionary page before him. He spelled aloud, "Re-spon—"

Just then Mrs. Beacham called from the farm kitchen, "Bobby! Come to supper."

The boy was absorbed in his study and did not hear the call. He continued spelling, "—si-bil-i-ty."

His brother bellowed, "Supper, Bobby!"

This time Robert heard. He marched out of the room spelling, "Re-spon-si-bil-i-ty."

Striding into the warm country kitchen, he exclaimed, "Look here, Dick! Please quit calling me Bobby. Anybody who can spell a big word like *responsibility* is no baby."

Dick Beacham walked over to the table, carrying a pitcher of milk. "Anybody who can spell that word really should know what it means," he teased. "I noticed, Bobby, that you haven't fed the hens or the calves. You haven't done any of your chores."

Robert scowled and clenched his fist. He said angrily to his eighteen-year-old brother, "My studying for the spelling match at school is more important than chores. Nothing on this whole big farm is as important as that spelldown—to me, at least."

Even as he spoke, Robert knew that he did not really mean what he said. But he would not admit it.

Mrs. Beacham stood at a kitchen window, anxiously observing the November weather. "Now, boys, don't argue," she said absent-mindedly over her shoulder. Then she went on, "Dad's outside studying the clouds. He is wondering whether to pick our corn or not. He'll never forgive himself if the corn isn't picked before it snows."

"According to the weatherman a big snow is headed our way," Dick said, stepping to the door to call his father to supper.

"For Dad's sake," sighed Mrs. Beacham, "I hope the weatherman is wrong. Think of our bushels of corn still in the field."

Corn was the money crop of the Beacham family. They had eighty acres of it, and it was not yet harvested. The neighbors, whose cornfields lay on higher ground, already had their corn in cribs. But everything had held back the Beacham crop this year.

In the first place, there had been a rainy spring. The soil in Mr. Beacham's field had remained too wet for plowing and planting for a long time. Then the summer and the early autumn had not been good seasons for corn-growing. They had been wet and cool. The late corn had needed the rain, but it also had to have sunny days and hot, dry nights to ripen properly before winter.

By the end of October, Mr. Beacham had begun to examine the corn daily to see if the ears were dry enough to pick. The corn had to be completely dried out before it was picked, or it would spoil in the crib.

Now it was the last part of November, and snow might come any day. If it did, the corn would be ruined. Mr. Beacham had to decide whether to pick his corn—dry or not—or to take a chance on the weather.

Mr. Beacham came into the kitchen soon after Dick's call to supper. "We pick corn tomorrow!" he announced to his family.

"Tomorrow!" cried Robert. "I can't miss the spelling match at school tomorrow!"

Mr. Beacham smiled. "Dick will be all the help I'll need," he said.

The next morning Robert waited near the gate for the school bus. He watched Dick and his dad, who were already at work. Dad was managing the corn picker, and Dick was using the small tractor to pull wagonloads of corn from the field to the crib.

All at once Robert saw his father driving the big tractor to the barnyard at high speed.

Near the gasoline pump he stopped and jumped quickly to the ground. Hastily he unhooked the hose from the gasoline pump and started to put gas in the tractor.

Suddenly Robert yelled in terror, "Dad! The engine! You forgot to turn it off!"

The warning came too late. While Robert yelled frantically and ran toward his father, gasoline spilled over the hot engine, and bright flames leaped up with an awful roar.

The next seconds were filled with panic. Mr. Beacham tore off his jacket to beat out the flames, and Dick sped from the crib with empty feed sacks. Shaking with fear, Mrs. Beacham and Robert watched as Dick and his father fought the raging fire.

When the terrible flames were out, Mrs. Beacham backed the car out of the garage and helped her husband into the front seat. "Dad's burned," she said to her sons. "I'm taking him to Dr. Hedges at Elder Grove."

In a voice filled with determination, Dick said, "Don't you worry about the corn, Dad. We'll get it in."

"Yes, we will," Robert echoed weakly.

As the car sped away, Robert thought of the spelling match he would miss. He did not say anything aloud. But to himself he argued, "Dad's corn really *is* more important."

Just then Dick exclaimed, "Well! Let's get going. I'll handle the picker. You put my last load of corn in the crib. Then haul the empty wagon to the field."

Robert shoveled the golden ears of corn into the crib elevator. Then he mounted the little tractor and drove to the field to trade his empty wagon for the one Dick was filling.

As Robert returned to the crib with more corn, he thought again of the spelling match. Disappointment hit him so keenly that it hurt. He shook off the feeling, though, and soon his work made him forget spelling entirely.

Back and forth went Robert, from the field to the crib, from the crib back to the field. He would hitch on a load, bounce over the rough ground, unload, and bounce to the field again, where Dick had another load of corn ready. Hour after hour the two boys toiled, harvesting corn as fast as they could.

On their way to the house for lunch they studied the sky anxiously. There was little to see but flocks of birds. Wise old ganders were winging their way southward, leading V-shaped wedges of honking geese. But there was a small, fluffy cloud in the northern sky. After lunch the boys noticed that the cloud had grown larger and darker.

"It looks bad," Robert said drearily.

Dick nodded. "Yes, it does," he agreed. "It'll probably snow before morning."

Robert gazed dismally at all the acres and acres of corn to be gathered and stored.

Suddenly Dick gave a shout.

"Look!" he cried. "All the machines in the neighborhood are coming down the road!"

Surely enough, a very strange parade was approaching. Advancing in a long line were tractors, wagons, and corn pickers. They all came rattling and creaking, bobbing and swinging from side to side right up to the gate that led into the cornfield.

Thomas Elferson, the Beachams' nearest neighbor, rode the lead tractor. He jumped down and walked briskly over to where Dick and Robert stood.

"I heard about your dad's getting hurt," he said. "We men in the community decided that we'd better help harvest your corn. A big snowstorm is going to hit here soon."

The friendly neighbor ran his eye over the acres already harvested. "Dick, you have really been working!" he cried. "You have harvested an amazing amount of corn."

Dick looked proudly toward his brother and answered, "I can't claim all the credit. My partner did his share. He did as much work as a man."

"Great!" exclaimed Mr. Elferson, clapping Robert on the shoulder. "I like to see a boy take responsibility. But now, young fellow, you need a rest. You've earned one. Run along to the house."

Robert limped wearily to the back porch and sat down. He saw the neighbors enter the cornfield. He watched their pickers start slashing into the rows of cornstalks.

Some time later Robert's mother drove into the yard. "Dad is going to be just fine," she said. "He's staying at the hospital overnight, though. One wrist is painfully burned."

Just then she looked toward the cornfield. "Oh, Bobby!" Mrs. Beacham gasped. "Our neighbors, bless them, came to help!"

Robert chuckled. He did not mind being called Bobby now. He had proved that he could do a man's job.

For a moment longer, Robert sat on the steps. Then, squaring his shoulders, he set off to start the evening chores. "With Dad hurt and Dick in the field, the chores are my responsibility," he said.

Moving Westward

Jonathan's Buffalo

In May, 1846, a wagon train started west-ward from Independence, Missouri. Among the hundreds of pioneers, none was happier than fifteen-year-old Jonathan Starbuck.

"Just imagine, Hawk Eye," he said to his pony, "we'll see prairies where buffaloes roam by the thousands! Maybe I can shoot one."

Jonathan was a brave boy, but he was glad to be making the long journey with many other people. Men who had returned from the West reported that the roads were nothing but rough trails. They described dangerous animals and told tales of savage Indians who roamed the plains.

The journey had been well planned. Each family owned a stout canvas-covered wagon pulled by oxen or horses. Only necessary things, such as guns, tools, farm implements, bedding, food, and dishes, were taken.

It was a thrilling day for Jonathan when the big wagon train set out. His sharp eyes noticed everything. The captain of the train started first. The other wagons followed him, one behind the other. The train was so long that people at the rear could not see the front end of it.

The wagons creaked and rumbled. Cows and calves, tied behind the wagons, mooed as they followed. Barking dogs ran alongside the train. The children shouted with excitement.

Each day of the journey was interesting to Jonathan. He particularly enjoyed riding out with his rifle to help the men hunt for game. He had formed a friendship with one of the guides, French Pierre. With Pierre's help, Jonathan was fast becoming a good shot.

Evenings in camp were the best part of the day. First the women and girls would begin to cook the game that the hunters had shot. While supper cooked, Jonathan and the other boys would help the men feed the animals and mend wagons and harness. After supper the travelers would gather around a huge campfire. There they sang gay songs or listened to stories that someone told.

Sometimes the fun was interrupted by the long, mournful howls of coyotes. Then the pioneers seated around the campfire would shudder as they gathered closer together in the friendly, warm firelight.

Week after week the train rumbled along. When a dangerous river had to be forded, the wagons could travel only a few miles a day. Then Jonathan would feel impatient. He was eager to get farther west to see the buffaloes.

One morning Jonathan was awakened by an unusual stir in camp. Pierre, who had been out early looking for game, came riding into camp excitedly. "Buffalo!" he shouted.

Jonathan and the other boys and men got dressed with lightning speed. They gobbled a few mouthfuls of breakfast and then quickly saddled their horses. Everyone was yelling, "Fresh meat! Roast buffalo for supper!"

Swiftly Jonathan urged his pony toward the place where the men were gathering. At last he would see some of the shaggy beasts that he had heard so much about!

Pierre pointed ahead, yelling to the men, "The buffalo are just over that swell!" As the men spurred their horses to the top of the rounded hill, Pierre called to Jonathan, "Get your rifle ready, Sharpshooter."

Suddenly Jonathan beheld a sight that made him gasp in amazement. Buffaloes—thousands of them! How magnificent they were!

Pierre cried, "Run your buffalo!" Yelling, the men poured down the slope. Before them the buffaloes raced wildly, their heavy heads low, their tails flying straight out.

A few seconds later Jonathan and the men reached the outer edge of the great herd. A brown sea of running buffaloes stretched off to one side of them across the plain. The pounding feet of the animals shook the earth. Thick clouds of dust swirled upward.

As they ran, the big, shaggy-maned beasts panted heavily, and their tongues hung loosely from their mouths. Above the deafening noise of their drumming hoofs rose the cries of the excited hunters.

An instant of panic seized Jonathan. What if the herd should stampede in his direction and his horse should stumble? The hoofs of the buffaloes would pound him into the plain!

Suddenly, as if a signal had been given, the great herd separated into half a dozen groups going off in as many directions. Some of the hunters followed one group, some another.

Jonathan was too absorbed in the hunt and too excited to notice that he had lost all his companions in the confusion. He picked out a fat buffalo. Spurring his horse, he lifted his rifle, took flying aim, and fired. The next moment the ground dropped from under him as Hawk Eye pitched into a gully.

At the bottom of the rocky gully the pinto mare stumbled, falling forward on her knees. But by grabbing the saddle horn just in time, Jonathan was able to keep in the saddle.

Quickly, Hawk Eye scrambled to her feet. She nearly slipped backward as she climbed the steep opposite bank. Then suddenly she was out of the gully and galloping after the rumbling herd.

On the buffaloes thundered in the flying dust. Jonathan picked out another animal and fired again. It was a good shot, not too high. Then, in trying to reload, he lost sight of his quarry. But he knew that the buffalo he had hit was seriously wounded. It would soon have to fall behind the rest of the herd.

The boy slowed up gradually in order to let the herd sweep past him while he waited for his wounded buffalo to drop out. Before long Jonathan spied a lone cow galloping heavily. Quickly he spurred his pony to the wounded beast's side.

The cow's eyes were reddened with rage, and her thick mane bristled. Before Jonathan could take aim, the beast savagely swung to attack him. But Hawk Eye dodged neatly.

Aiming carefully, the boy fired once more. The cow sank to her knees, then rolled over and lay still. Jonathan had shot a buffalo!

With one leap Jonathan was on the ground. In triumph he raced over to examine his kill. Then the lad straightened up and looked about him. The herd was fast vanishing from sight. Not a hunter could be seen on the prairie.

Suddenly Jonathan realized that he was all alone—alone with a dead buffalo on a silent, deserted plain! He did not know how far he had ridden or whether he was north, south, east, or west of the wagon train. The rolling plain offered no landmark to guide him. As far as his eye could see, there was nothing but sand hills covered with scrubby grass.

Jonathan felt a moment of horrible panic. Then he grew more calm. After all, he had a horse, a weapon, and fresh meat. Maybe at dusk he could see the fires of the wagon train. Or Hawk Eye's fine sense of direction might get them safely back to camp.

He decided to try to skin the buffalo while the horse rested. With his hunting knife he hacked away at the tough hide. All at once he started to remember ugly stories he had heard about hunters lost on the plains. His thoughts made the knife shake in his hands.

Suddenly from somewhere beyond the rise, Jonathan heard the hoofbeats of a galloping horse. Were Indians coming?

Terror swept over him like a flood. With shaking hands Jonathan loaded his rifle. He set his back to the horse and stood with the weapon ready. His heart beat wildly as he waited to see who would come over the rise.

It was Pierre! With one glance the guide took in Jonathan's plight—his winded horse and the dead buffalo at his feet.

"I'm not lost, Pierre," the boy said quickly.

"I know you're not lost, son," Pierre said with a twinkle in his eye. "Thought I'd just come and help you pack some of your buffalo back to camp."

Homesick Honey

"I'm homesick for Indiana," thought Nora Beeman. She was sitting outdoors near her new western home, twisting wisps of grass into tight bunches for the cookstove. Here on the prairie, trees were so scarce that wood was too precious to burn.

At last Nora finished her tedious task and said, "There, that should be enough to bake Mother's pumpkin pies."

The flat, open prairie made Nora miss the trees that had surrounded her big brick home in eastern Indiana. And she was not used to her tiny prairie home. It seemed odd to be living in a house made of sod. Even the roof was sod-covered instead of shingled.

Nora's father had plowed large chunks of sod out of the earth. Using these sod chunks for bricks, he had built the house along a low ridge as a protection against the strong winds on the prairie. Alongside the house he had made a sod barn, too, even though the family had few animals to keep in it just now.

The Beemans' big red barn in Indiana had sheltered many animals. Some of them had been Nora's special pets. "If I had a pet," she sighed, "I wouldn't be so lonesome."

Suddenly Nora's sharp eyes spied someone approaching on horseback. "Company!" she shouted excitedly. "Company is coming!"

Nora's mother and father and her two little brothers came running out of the small soddy. Standing together in the autumn sunshine, the family eagerly waited to greet the visitor.

"It's Alva Majors," observed Mr. Beeman. Mr. Majors lived about three miles away. He was the Beemans' nearest neighbor.

"Hello! I have a present for you," called Mr. Majors as he rode up. He pointed to a long-legged little calf that was tagging along beside his horse.

"What a darling calf!" cried Nora. Then she ran up to the calf and snuggled her face against its neck. It felt as soft as a kitten.

"She'll grow into a fine cow," Mr. Majors told the delighted family. "Soon you will have plenty of good milk and cream."

"She needs a name," said Mrs. Beeman.

Dimples danced in Nora's cheeks as she giggled, "Oh, I know a fine name! She is so sweet—let's call her Honey."

Mr. Majors chatted a while, then started home. Immediately Honey started after him.

"Come back, Honey!" Nora called to the calf. "Please come home!" But Honey did not obey. Finally Mr. Majors spurred his horse toward the calf, driving her back again.

"Keep Honey locked up for a few days," Mr. Majors said to Nora. "She'll be a little homesick at first until she gets used to her new home. Then she won't stray away."

Nora put Honey in the barn. But the next morning someone neglected to close the door. The calf bounced out, startling the Beemans' only rooster. With a loud cock-a-doodle-doo, the poor fowl flew up on the barn.

Hearing the noise, Nora dashed out of the sod house and saw Honey racing toward her old home. Nora finally caught the calf and tied it in the barn, saying sternly, "Now you stay here! After all, I'm homesick, too. But you don't see me running off to Indiana."

Alas, the naughty calf learned to wriggle out of the rope around her neck. Whenever the barn door was open, she ran back to Mr. Majors' farm. Then Mr. Beeman had to go after her. It was most vexing.

"This is ridiculous!" Mr. Beeman said one day. "I haven't time to chase that silly calf. We'd better give her back to Mr. Majors."

But Nora pleaded so hard that her father agreed to give Honey another chance.

A week later, Mr. Beeman had to leave his family and journey to the nearest town to sell a load of oats and to buy winter supplies.

That afternoon, gray clouds appeared on the horizon. Mrs. Beeman and Nora decided to pump some water and bring it in before the storm started. But upon reaching the pump, they discovered an alarming thing. The pump was broken! They could get no water!

"Let's lift the cover off the well and draw water with a bucket on a rope," said Nora.

The wooden lid was very heavy. As Mrs. Beeman and her daughter struggled to lift it, it slipped from their hands and jammed in the well opening. No matter how they tried, they could not budge the lid. "We need horses to move it now," said Mrs. Beeman with a hint of worry in her voice. "Dad won't be back with our team for several days. We're lucky it's going to rain. We will put out tubs and kettles for the rain to fill with water."

Instead of rain, the storm brought snow in little dry flakes that blew this way and that, mixing with the dust. Not even a small cupful could be gathered up to melt for water.

The next day an icy wind was still blowing. Mrs. Beeman said anxiously, "If we could get word to Mr. Majors, he'd help us."

Suddenly Nora had an idea. "Mother," she said, "we can tie a message to Honey and let her run back to her old home."

"Yes, but Mr. Majors may not notice her among his own calves," said Mrs. Beeman.

Nora had an idea for that, too. From red trimmings on two hats, she made a ribbon halter for Honey and decorated it with roses and a bow. She tied a note to the halter. Then she put some pebbles in a pail and tied it to Honey's neck to make a rattling noise.

After letting Honey out of the barn, Nora stamped her foot and waved her shawl. "Go ahead!" she said firmly. "Run away!"

Honey did just what was expected. Quick as a wink, she ran off to her old home.

Mr. Majors, too, did what was expected. As soon as the unusual messenger attracted his attention, he read the note and rushed to help his neighbors.

When Mr. Beeman came home and heard the tale, he said, "Honey deserves a reward. She should be allowed to stay in the home she loves."

"Yes," said Nora, gulping a sob.

A day later Nora was in the barn watching her father shoe a horse. As she gazed sadly at Honey's empty stall, something nuzzled her elbow. Nora turned and was amazed to see Honey. ".Honey's back!" she cried joyfully.

"Well," laughed Mr. Beeman, "I guess Honey has decided that *this* is the home she likes!"

"Yes," said Nora, hugging the calf. "She's not homesick any more." Then she murmured in surprise, "And neither am I. Honey and I have both learned to love our new home!"

Bill Meets a Longhorn

Dodge City, Kansas, looked exciting to Bill Fisher as he rode his pony, Duke, into town ahead of his family's big covered wagon. Bill was thinking, "I hope I'll see a cowboy while we wait here for a wagon train going west."

All the way from Ohio, Bill's conversation had been mainly about cowboys and longhorn cattle. After the family had found a camping place, he asked, "Now will I see a cowboy?"

"Dodge City is one of the best places in the West to see cowboys," laughed Mr. Fisher. "They all stop here when they drive their big herds of longhorns north to summer pasture or to the railroad to be shipped east."

"Oh, wonderful!" cried Bill. "Now I'll find out if longhorns are as fierce as people say."

Early the next day Bill saddled Duke and set out to find a cowboy. Duke was old, but Bill was proud of him because he had once been a cow pony. While traveling west, Bill had practiced whirling a lasso and vaulting into the saddle. He now felt that both he and Duke were ready to herd cattle.

Riding about Dodge City, Bill soon spied a cowboy. He was standing beside his pony at a hitching post, adjusting his stirrup. Bill stopped and watched a moment. Then he said shyly, "Good morning!"

The cowboy turned around and grinned at Bill. "Morning, Shorty!" he said.

Bill began asking questions so fast that the man had to answer them all at once. "I am Cactus Jones, foreman of the Lazy K Ranch in Wyoming," he said. "We're camping here until a herd of longhorns gets in from Texas tomorrow. We'll cut the herd and drive part of it to Wyoming and part to Montana."

When Bill started to ask another question, Cactus said, "See here, Shorty! You have enough questions for twenty men to answer. Why not ride out to camp with me and spread the questions around among all the boys?"

Eagerly Bill rode out to the Lazy K camp. All day he listened spellbound as the cowboys talked about the coming cattle drive. At dusk Bill rode back to Dodge City, tired but happy.

The next day Bill returned to the cowboys' camp just as the Texas herd arrived. The place was buzzing with excitement. He halted Duke and listened to Cactus giving orders.

Suddenly Cactus saw Bill. "Just what are you doing here, young fellow?" he asked.

Bill sat up tall in the saddle and tried to look very grown-up. "I thought maybe you could use an extra cowboy today," he said.

Cactus roared with laughter. Then suddenly he grew very serious. Pointing to the herd, he declared, "Those beasts are mighty mean. You had better head back for Dodge City as fast as that old pony can carry you!"

"Can't I even watch you?" begged Bill.

The disappointment on Bill's face was too much for Cactus. "I guess you can watch if you keep far enough away," he said gruffly.

"Oh, thanks! Thanks a lot!" cried Bill.

Then Cactus said, "Your horse knows his business. So just let him do your thinking for you. And remember—*don't* get off your horse. A man on foot seems to drive these wild longhorns crazy. When they attack, they don't leave much behind them but pieces."

Bill listened to the orders meekly.

"Keep toward the head of the herd and to the left," Cactus added. "From there you can see how the men cut the herd in two."

As he rode toward the head of the herd, Bill decided that stories about longhorns were not exaggerated. A few steers had horns that spread nearly seven feet. They had shaggy foreheads, wild eyes, and powerful muscles.

Bill rode Duke to a slight rise of ground and watched the cattle as they trailed after the lead steer in clouds of dust. They walked singly, two or three abreast, or in groups of five or six. They made a long string that stretched nearly a mile across the prairie.

Cowboys rode on either side of the line to keep the cattle from leaving the herd. Often a rider would dart into the line like a streak of lightning. He would head off an animal that was breaking away or urge a slow one along.

Bill noticed the cowboys ahead of the line who would separate the cattle into two herds. As the lead steer approached these men, he stopped and pawed the ground.

Instantly two riders crowded toward him swinging their lassos. The steer whirled to the left to avoid being roped and then quieted down again. The steer behind the lead steer was turned to the right, the next two animals were turned to the left, and so on. No detail of the cutting escaped Bill's admiring eyes.

Bill could hear the droning voices of men counting the cattle as they separated into two lines.

The day was warm, and everything seemed to be going peacefully as the cattle counters droned on. Bill relaxed in the saddle and let his pony's reins hang loose. Duke could be depended upon not to get into trouble.

But suddenly the horse was surprised by a quick bite from a horsefly. His hind hoofs shot upward. Bill, caught entirely off guard, could not avoid being thrown forward against the saddle horn. His hat went sailing over Duke's nose and landed on the ground.

Bill was dazed by the jolt, and it took him several minutes to recover. He rubbed his stomach as he looked at his hat lying on the ground in front of him. But he did not get off his horse to pick it up. The warning Cactus had given him was still fresh in Bill's mind.

The wearisome counting of the cattle went on and on. The sun felt hotter and hotter on Bill's bare head. He waited impatiently for the cutting to be finished. "Being a cowboy isn't all fun," he sighed to himself.

Finally all but three steers in the long line of cattle had passed. Bill looked longingly at his hat in the dust. "The counting is about over," he thought. He felt sure it was safe to get off his horse and pick up the hat.

Quickly, Bill dismounted. Holding Duke's reins, he reached for the hat. As he did so, the last three steers in the long line stopped. They stared at Bill threateningly. But he did not see them because he was bending over.

Just then Dusty Carter, one of the counters, caught sight of Bill. He yelled wildly, "Hey! Get back on your horse! Get back on your horse! You'll be killed!"

Hat in hand, Bill whirled about to see what had made Dusty yell. One of the steers had humped his back and was heading in Bill's direction. As the steer broke into a run, he twisted his neck so that one horn extended directly in front of him near the ground.

Immediately Bill realized his peril. Faster than he had ever moved in his life, he vaulted into the saddle. At that moment Duke swung sharply out of the way of the dangerous beast.

As Duke turned, Bill had a confusing vision of galloping cowboys swinging their lassos. They seemed to have suddenly appeared out of nowhere. At the same instant three ropes sailed toward the longhorn.

The galloping horses came to a sudden halt. With stiffened legs they dug their front hoofs into the dirt and met the pull that came when the lassos hit their mark. The charging steer crashed to earth with a thump, and the whole incident was over.

When Bill saw Cactus riding toward him, he prepared for a scolding. But after one look at Bill's white face, all Cactus said was, "You're good at getting into a saddle, aren't you, Tenderfoot?"

Bill glanced down at the panting, wild-eyed steer. He swallowed hard before he spoke. In a shaky voice he said, "I am afraid that I'm better at getting into a saddle than staying in one. I guess I still have a lot to learn about being a cowboy."

Treasure in the Covered Wagon

Off for Independence

Flave-Ann Stone watched her mother and father packing the two covered wagons for the long journey to Oregon. Mrs. Stone was about to put an armful of quilts in one wagon. "Getting all the things from a big farmhouse into two wagons is no easy job," she said.

Flave-Ann thought, "I wonder where we'll put my organ. Pa is so busy he might get cross if I ask about it just now."

But as she watched the wagon space being filled with food, bedding, and tools, she grew anxious. There just had to be room for her little reed organ. She simply could not bear to leave it behind in Missouri.

111

Adapted and abridged by permission of the publisher, J. B. Lippincott Company, from *Treasure in the Covered Wagon* by Vera Graham. Copyright, 1952, by Vera Graham.

By evening the wagons were nearly loaded. While Pa and Flave-Ann's brother Dan tied a water barrel onto one wagon, Flave-Ann climbed up on a wheel of the other one. She saw that it was packed almost to the top.

"Pa didn't leave room for my organ!" she cried. Numb with disappointment, Flave-Ann climbed down and stood near Ma.

"We won't have room for all the things we really need, Flave-Ann," said Ma. "Do you think the organ is that important to everyone? I'm afraid you are a selfish girl."

"I don't mean to be selfish, Ma," Flave-Ann said as tears rolled down her cheeks.

Just then Pa finished tying the barrel to the other wagon. He called to Flave-Ann, and she quickly dried her eyes. "Flave-Ann," he said, "come and see if you think the organ will fit into this space I've saved for it."

Flave-Ann ran to Pa. She laughed and cried and jumped up and down. "Oh, Pa! You did remember!" she exclaimed.

That night in her bed, Flave-Ann thought, "Everything is going to be all right. My little organ and I will travel to Oregon together."

The next day the family set out. Dan rode in the ox-drawn wagon. Flave-Ann, Ma, and Pa rode in the one pulled by horses. That night they reached Independence, Missouri. There they joined a big train of wagons and met Trader Jim, who would lead them west.

Jim inspected each wagon to see if it was too heavily loaded. "What do you expect to do with a music box?" he teased Flave-Ann. Then noticing her worried look, he smiled.

The train left Independence on April 10, 1845. Flave-Ann learned that traveling was often wearisome. Sometimes the trail was so rough that she was afraid the organ would have to be left behind to lighten the horses' load. But it was still safe in the wagon.

Crossing the Platte

One cold, wet day in June, the wagon train reached the Platte River and halted to prepare for the crossing, early the next day. When the rain ceased, the men went to cut strong timbers that might be needed for fording the shallow river. The children romped, and the women hung rain-soaked bedding out to dry.

Next day at sunrise, Flave-Ann was sitting with Ma on the wagon seat. At breakfast Pa had said, "It will take a full day to cross the Platte, even if we have good luck."

Flave-Ann, fascinated by the scene around her, watched Pa help Trader Jim line up the big wagons for the crossing. Astride one of Jim's horses, Mr. Stone was riding up and down the long train. Soon the wagons were lined up. The yoked oxen moved restlessly. The horses pranced in their traces.

"Hold the horses right here until I signal," Pa called to Ma from his horse. Then he rode up ahead and started several wagons across the river. "Keep in line there!" Pa yelled as he rode beside the moving wagons.

When Pa came back, he said to Ma, "The river bed is soft in places. Each wagon will have to use extra horses to get across."

Just then Trader Jim rode up to discuss the problem with Pa. Jim studied the load in Ma's wagon with experienced eyes and said, "Try two more horses on this wagon. We will have to put twelve or fourteen oxen or horses on the heaviest loads."

Dan and the other drivers unhitched their teams to use on the wagons up ahead. Then they went to help the other wagons across.

Flave-Ann gazed across the big river. The water sparkled in the sunlight, and the trees bordering the opposite bank seemed far away. "Pa says the Platte is a mile wide. We'll get over all right, won't we, Ma?" Flave-Ann asked anxiously. "We just have to!"

Ma did not answer. "Whoa!" she shouted to the horses as she waited for Pa's signal.

Then Pa signaled, and Ma started across the river. "Hold on, Flave-Ann," she said.

The horses strained and pulled in the deep sand. The heavy wagon jerked, and things inside got out of place and rattled about.

Then the wagon hit a sand bar. The organ began to rock. "Oh, help!" cried Flave-Ann, scrambling back to the organ. "It's falling!" She leaned against it to brace it, but as the horses halted, the organ righted itself.

Ma yelled to the horses. They pulled as hard as they could. But the wagon wheels just sank lower into the sand. The horses began to flounder in the water.

"Pa!" Ma cried. "Come help me, quick!"

Pa and some of the other men brought cut timbers and laid them on the river bed. With shoulders against the wagon wheels, the men yelled, "Ready! Heave!" Finally, the wagon was heaved up onto the timbers.

Then two more teams were hitched to the Stones' wagon. As it moved on across the river, Trader Jim rode up alongside. "Looks like we'll get that old music box across the river after all," he teased Flave-Ann. "Were you scared, young lady?"

"I surely was!" said Flave-Ann. "What made the wagon sink down, Trader Jim?"

"You hit a hole in the river bed that was filled with sand," Jim replied. Then he rode back to help the remaining wagons get across.

When Ma's wagon reached the other side, she cracked her whip and urged the horses up the bank. Flave-Ann clung to the seat as the wagon bumped over the rough ground.

Pa saw them safely on the bank. "Now you rest a bit," he said to Ma, patting her hand. "It's been a hard morning."

Later when Dan got across with his wagon, he said, "Pa says we'll be here at least two days. It will take us until sundown to get the rest of the wagons across."

That night as Flave-Ann climbed into bed, she whispered happily, "Well, we're across the Platte, little organ. And you're still safe."

The next day Pa said to Flave-Ann, "How would you like to play for a dance tonight?"

Flave-Ann almost choked with excitement. "Do you really mean it?" she cried joyously.

Eagerly she watched the men construct the dance platform. Would evening ever come?

Soon after sundown the camp was buzzing. Girls in their best dresses gathered near the organ at the end of the platform. "Oh, how pretty everyone looks!" cried Flave-Ann.

When Flave-Ann sat down at the organ, a boy with a fiddle joined her, and they began to play. While gay couples filled the dance floor, the square-dance caller shouted, "Get your partners! All join hands!"

People on the side lines clapped and sang as the dancers swung in a dizzy whirl. The men's heavy shoes clumped on the rough log platform, and the girls' full skirts billowed out. Faster and faster whirled the dancers, far into the night. It would be a long time before there would be another occasion for such fun.

The Trail Divides

After crossing dangerous mountain passes, the wagon train reached Fort Bridger late in July. Here supplies were bought, and the train divided. Some people took the trail to California. Others were going on to Oregon.

Before the California wagons left the camp, Flave-Ann played her organ at a good-by sing.

"That's a good send-off!" the people said.

The wagons bound for California carried many water barrels. Trader Jim said that when they got to the Great Salt Desert there would be no water for more than sixty miles.

Then Flave-Ann heard that water might be scarce along the Oregon Trail, too. "If Pa decides to carry water barrels," she worried, "he may have to leave the organ behind!"

Pa did fasten extra barrels of water onto the wagons before starting off on the Oregon Trail. But the organ was not left behind.

During the journey to Fort Hall, traveling conditions grew more and more disagreeable for the pioneers. Water was scarce. Sand swirled in dusty circles around the wagons. Miles seemed endless on the hot, dry trail.

Many people fell ill from lack of water, and some lost courage. At night when Flave-Ann ached with weariness, someone would always ask, "How about some music, Flave-Ann?"

She never refused, and after the first tune she always felt more rested. "I'm so thankful we have the organ," she told Ma. "It seems to cheer folks more than anything else."

"Yes," said Ma. "I'm sorry I called you selfish. You help us all with your music."

Each day it grew harder for the exhausted oxen and horses to pull the heavy wagons. One night the men decided that furniture and heavy articles would have to be left behind.

Flave-Ann was sick at heart. "I must be brave if they leave the organ," she thought. "But how can I live without it?"

The next day Flave-Ann fought tears as unloaded furniture was placed beside a sign left for pioneers who would pass by later.

Then she saw the weary travelers moving toward the wagon that held the little organ. Standing in a quiet circle around Trader Jim, they, too, were wondering about the organ.

An old man with a grizzled beard, who had driven all the way in a one-horse cart, spoke up. "I can carry that wee organ in my cart. I walk most of the time anyway," he said.

Trader Jim thanked the old man and said, "We'll just leave it in the wagon for now."

The travelers looked very dismal. So Jim said gently, "Let's have a tune, Flave-Ann."

Flave-Ann climbed into the covered wagon and began playing all the favorite trail songs. None of them sounded as gay as they usually did. But the soft tones floating off over the sandy plains made the people feel better.

Before bedtime that night, Flave-Ann ran her hand over the smooth, polished top of the organ. "I won't have to worry about you any more, little organ," she said. "You're really everybody's organ, not just mine."

Flave-Ann knew now that the people in the wagon train loved the organ and needed it as much as she did. She knew they would not allow it to be left behind on the Oregon Trail.

"Pike's Peak or Bust"

In the middle of his morning farm chores, Bob Barker suddenly asked his father, "Dad, why don't we go to Pike's Peak and hunt for gold? Half our neighbors are leaving Illinois, and people from the East pass by each week."

"Oho," laughed Mr. Barker. "So you have caught the gold fever! Well, Son, to tell the truth, so have I. But it's over a thousand miles to the Peak. I'd have to plan such a long trip by covered wagon very carefully, or it would be hard for your mother and sisters."

"They want to go!" cried Bob. "I have asked them. They say they'd like to see the Rocky Mountains and the land west of here."

In 1859 and 1860 it seemed that everyone east of the Rockies was rushing west to the gold fields. Finally Bob's father decided to go west, too. Joining a big wagon train, the Barkers traveled with other farmers and with bankers, doctors, teachers, and shopkeepers.

Like the Barkers, many people had sturdy canvas-covered wagons with "Pike's Peak or Bust" painted on the sides. Some had only old oxcarts, farm wagons, or buggies. Many had livestock trailing behind their vehicles. It was an odd-looking band, but a merry one.

Several times during the first days of the journey, Bob said, "When we get to Cherry Creek, I'm going right out and dig for gold. I wish the oxen would go faster. Maybe all the gold will be mined before we get there."

"Well, Son," his father answered, "even if there isn't as much gold as people say, I'm sure there'll be lots of horses. And horses must be shod. I brought along my blacksmith tools. I can make some money that way."

The idea of being a blacksmith in the gold fields made Bob laugh. The only thing to do in a place like that was to dig for gold!

Journeying on the rough trail was not easy. Sometimes savage storms hit the train. Often water was scarce. Some of the people fell ill. The horses and oxen grew thin and weak.

As the travelers approached Colorado, they began to meet disappointed people coming back from the gold fields. "That gold is just talk," they said. "Better go back home."

But Mr. Barker was certain that he could support his family, even if he did not find gold. Bob still planned to hunt gold.

They began seeing quite a few broken-down outfits. One day they saw a wagon that had one front wheel gone and no animal to pull it. The owner was just sitting there, trying to decide what to do.

Bundling up a few belongings, the stranger joined the big wagon train. The discouraged man's plight made Bob thankful that his father had planned the family's journey carefully.

The last week of the trip, the Barkers met Mr. Byers, who was hauling a printing press and cases of type in his wagon. Mr. Byers had been a surveyor in Nebraska, but he was going to start a newspaper in Colorado.

Bob chuckled about Mr. Byers' plan. Why would anyone spend all his time publishing a newspaper when he could be digging gold?

"A newspaper should do well in the gold fields," said Mr. Byers. "Folks there will be eager for news." Then he added, "Bob, I need a hard-working boy like you to assist me. Would you care to take the job?"

"No, thank you, Mr. Byers," Bob replied. "I'm going to hunt for gold in Colorado."

"Maybe you'd better accept his offer, Bob," said Mr. Barker. "You'll need tools to dig gold, and I haven't money to buy them now."

Bob thought a moment. Then he agreed to work for Mr. Byers. He soon would earn money enough to try his luck at digging gold.

When the Barkers finally reached Colorado, they learned that only a few men were finding gold. Mr. Barker lost no time in setting up a blacksmith shop to support his family.

Mr. Byers and Bob faced a problem when they began making plans for the newspaper. Two settlements had sprung up on Cherry Creek—Denver on one side, Auraria on the other. Because of great rivalry between the towns, Mr. Byers knew that if the newspaper was to succeed, it must not take sides.

Bob had an idea. "Let's build our shop in the creek, between Denver and Auraria," he said. "Then we won't be taking sides."

Mr. Byers agreed. A small office was built on posts driven into the creek bed, and work began on Colorado's first newspaper. Mr. Byers published articles about gold strikes and other news of interest to the miners.

Bob discovered, as he helped set the type, that he liked newspaper work. Yet he still longed to hunt for gold, and he often dreamed of the day when he would strike it rich.

But when the first newspaper rolled off the press, Bob had little time to dream of gold.

"Rocky Mountain News!" yelled Bob as he sold the papers. The miners of Denver and Auraria were glad to pay twenty-five cents for a newspaper. It was the first one that some of them had seen for many months.

For a time the *Rocky Mountain News* did well. Then disaster struck. A cloudburst in the hills sent a whirling flood of water down Cherry Creek. Mr. Byers managed to rescue his press and some of his type, but the little printing shop in the stream was washed away.

What to do next was the question.

Again Bob had an idea. He said, "Why not travel to the different mining camps with our outfit, Mr. Byers, printing news as we go?"

Mr. Byers thought the idea was excellent. He and Bob packed the printing outfit on the backs of burros. Then they set out for the camps. Bob's eyes were sparkling. At last he would get to see the miners at work.

One morning the traveling printers arrived at a camp high up in the mountains just in time to hear a miner shout, "We've got it! At last we've got it!"

Bob jumped from his burro and ran over to the shouting miner. Excitedly the man told Bob that he was sure he had just struck the richest gold deposit yet found in Colorado.

Bob borrowed a fast horse from one of the miners. Quickly he rode back down the trail to Denver and Auraria with the news. When the miners heard about the rich deposit, they went wild with joy. Immediately many eager men started for the newest strike.

That gold strike marked a turning point for Colorado. More and more gold was found, and people poured into the twin towns near the mines. After a while the two settlements united to form the city of Denver.

Bob was so busy reporting all these events that he had no time to think about hunting for gold. Then one day he surprised even himself with another idea. "Mr. Byers," he said, "I like reporting the news so much that I've decided to become a newspaper man."

Mr. Byers laughed. "Bob, I'm afraid that's one of your ideas you can't carry out. You can't *become* a newspaper man because you are one already, and a good one, too!"

Drums in the Forest

One morning Andy York and Zeke Shelter were beside Zeke's cabin talking with their Indian friend, Watam. "Say, Watam," said Andy, "could you teach Zeke and me how to make a real Indian drum?"

"Yes, I'd be glad to," replied the Indian boy. And Watam's dark eyes sparkled with pleasure.

"We could use the drum to send messages to each other!" Andy said excitedly.

"That's a wonderful idea!" exclaimed Zeke. "Let's start making the drum right now."

"Good!" said Watam. "But first we need a big log."

The three boys got up and walked over to the woodpile at the end of the cabin. Watam picked out a large log. Then Zeke and Andy helped him cut a two-foot length from it with Mr. Shelter's crosscut saw.

Next the boys rolled the piece of log into a clearing near the ditch in front of the cabin. "Now we must build a fire," said Watam.

After the blazing fire had died down, Watam raked coals from the ashes and put them on one end of the log. As the coals lost heat, he scraped out the scorched wood. Again and again the boys heaped glowing coals in the hollow and scraped out the wood. Finally Watam said, "Now it is hollow enough."

Zeke went to a shed where his father kept hides that had not been tanned. He brought back an elkskin from which the hair had been removed. The boys stretched part of the skin over the open end of the log. Then they tied it firmly in place with a long strip of hide.

"There, it is finished," said Watam as he ran his hand lightly over the new drumhead. "Do not strike it until the elkskin dries hard. Then you will have an Indian drum."

"How far can it be heard?" asked Andy.

"The sound can be heard for many miles," Watam replied confidently.

"You know," remarked Zeke, "I think we should each have a signal drum. Andy and I live half a mile apart. And it's a mile from here to where you live, Watam. If we made a drum for each of us, we could talk to each other without running our legs off."

So the boys hollowed out two more pieces of the log. Watam then explained how water could be used to give each drum a different tone. "We didn't put water in the first drum, so it has a low tone. That one will be for Andy. We will fill Zeke's drum half full of water before we put the top on. It will have a middle tone. When I get mine home, I'll fill it nearly full to give it a high tone."

Then Watam discussed signals. "A slow, steady beat will mean *I must stay home and work*. A fast beat will mean *Come and visit*. Three beats and a pause, three beats and a pause will mean *I am in bad trouble. Come quickly and help me*. But we'll use this last signal only if we are in real danger."

The next day Andy visited Zeke again.

"Wouldn't it be fun to fool Watam?" Zeke said. "Let's beat out a trouble signal."

"That's not a good idea," protested Andy. "What if we really need help sometime?"

In a mischievous mood Zeke hooted, "Ah, we won't get into any trouble. Let's try my drum!" And he began to beat out the signal.

Then suddenly the new drumhead loosened. While the boys worked to repair it, Watam appeared, breathless from running.

"Trouble so soon?" he asked suspiciously.

"Yes," laughed Zeke. "I broke my drum."

"It's his own fault!" Andy said to Watam. "You told him to wait until the skin dried."

"You signaled me for that?" Watam cried. "You made me lose a big fish that I've been trying to catch for a long time." Then with his eyes flashing anger, Watam departed.

Zeke turned to Andy and jeered, "Watam is so serious he can't even take a joke."

At Andy's home a week later, Mrs. York gave Andy an empty molasses jug and half a slab of smoked bacon to take to Mr. Peal. "He'll fill the jug with syrup," she explained. "We're trading him the bacon for it. Hurry so you'll get home before dark."

Andy threaded his belt through the handle on the jug. Then he fastened the belt snugly with the jug hanging at his side. He tucked the bacon under his arm and set off through the forest for Mr. Peal's cabin.

When Andy reached Otter Creek, he felt thirsty. He knelt in the damp ferns beside the stream. Laying his slab of bacon down, he stretched out on some velvety moss to drink.

Suddenly his alert ears heard a creature moving in the bushes. "Maybe it's a moose," Andy thought. As the sound was repeated, he grabbed the bacon and stood up.

Andy was half expecting broad antlers to push through the thicket. But what actually *did* appear was a huge black bear.

It poked its head through the green leaves, sniffed loudly, and stared at Andy.

With a yell, the boy leaped over the creek. The bear bolted back into the bushes.

Andy raced down the trail toward the Peal cabin. Ahead of him a grazing doe and her frisky fawn caught the scent of the bear and bounded gracefully away into the trees.

Andy glanced back fearfully. He saw the huge bear emerge from the bushes and come across the creek. With a sinking feeling in his stomach, Andy hunted for a rock to hurl.

It was now apparent to Andy that the bear meant to pursue him. It kept lumbering along uncomfortably close to his heels.

Desperately Andy shouted at the beast. It did not go away. He flung a big rock at the bear. But it was not frightened. Andy sped toward a slender tree a short distance away. As he ran, he tucked the heavy slab of bacon into the front of his shirt where it would not hinder his movements. Hastily he climbed the sapling to a point well above the ground.

Out of peril for the moment, Andy wiped his moist face on his sleeve and looked down. The bear was circling the tree.

The heavy jug hanging on Andy's belt made him uncomfortable. As he started to remove the jug, it slipped and fell to the ground.

The startled bear dashed for cover. But it soon reappeared. It picked up the jug in its clumsy forepaws. With a curling pink tongue, it licked the container. Then it nibbled at the stopper. Finally the animal dropped the jug and put its forefeet against the tree. It did not try to climb up. It seemed to know that the sapling could not support it.

Anxiously, Andy began to notice signs of coming nightfall. A solitary owl hooted and flew away in search of prey. Above, in a red-orange sky, cawing crows winged southward. It occurred to Andy that the bear might lurk under the tree all night.

Finally the boy decided to try shouting, though he doubted that his voice would carry far enough for anyone to hear.

Andy yelled and yelled. His only answer was the spooky echo of his voice in the darkening forest.

138

Realizing that further shouting would be in vain, Andy quit yelling. Then the silence of the forest was broken only by the chirping of crickets among the ferns and by the lonely cry of a loon deep in the woods.

A cool wind swayed the trees. Shivering, Andy thought of the warm hearth in his home and of the tempting odor of the wild duckling that his mother would be roasting for supper.

Just then the bear grunted. Andy glanced down at it nervously. "Only a wizard could get himself out of this mess!" he muttered.

He thought of tossing the bacon to the bear. While the bear ate, he could climb down and run home. But that seemed risky. The bear might follow and pounce on him in the dark.

Andy changed his position on the limb of the sapling and looked at the trees nearby. To his left he saw a storm-damaged spruce. Half its trunk was hollow. As Andy surveyed the big spruce, he thought, "It reminds me of the log we hollowed out when we made our drums. I wish I had my drum now. I'd signal for help. Watam or Zeke would hear and bring someone to chase this bear away."

"But I haven't my drum," Andy reminded himself firmly. "And I can't wish my way out of this fix." He peered anxiously downward once more. In the dim light the bear's dark form was getting hard to see.

Then his glance drifted over to the hollow spruce again. As Andy studied it, his eyes brightened. "Maybe I can reach that tree," he thought. "I can break off a small limb and hammer out a signal for help on the hollow trunk. It won't be as good as a drum. But the sound might carry farther than my voice."

Immediately Andy took a firm hold on the sapling and started to swing it back and forth. He swayed the small tree until it started to bend toward a limb of the spruce. Each time that he came close, Andy would reach across the space between the trees. After several unsuccessful tries, he finally managed to grab the limb.

Monkeylike, Andy swung from the sapling to the spruce. Carefully he worked his way along the limb to the trunk. He kicked at a dead limb below him. Before he could grab it, the limb fell to the ground with a thud.

Andy began to hunt for another dry, dead limb. But a movement in the branches below made him glance down. The menacing beast had moved from the sapling. It was climbing the thick trunk of the spruce.

Andy frantically clutched a short dead limb and snapped it from the trunk. Then throwing one arm around the tree to brace himself, he began to pound out a trouble signal. Desperately he struck the hollow trunk of the spruce— three beats and a pause, three beats and a pause.

From time to time Andy looked down at the bear. The hollow thumping noise of Andy's pounding seemed to fascinate the big animal. Motionless, it clung to the tree and glared up at the frightened boy.

Andy kept pounding steadily. The noise made his ears ring. The muscles in his arm throbbed. But he did not slacken his efforts. He clenched his teeth and kept beating out the signal. Twice he hammered so hard that he barely avoided losing his balance and falling through the tree branches to the ground.

Suddenly Andy caught a glimpse of a light. It was bobbing around and flickering in the darkness between him and his home. The light disappeared and reappeared. It moved about uncertainly. Andy shouted wildly and began pounding the tree with all his might.

Then he heard people shouting. The dry brush crackled a few rods away as footsteps approached. Andy recognized the voices of his father, Zeke, Mr. Shelter, and Watam.

Frightened by all the noise, the bear did not linger. Quickly the beast slid to the ground and bounded away in the darkness.

The flickering lantern reached the foot of the spruce. Andy climbed down and stood on unsteady legs in the midst of his rescuers.

Watam said, "I was at Zeke's when we heard your signal. You'd never fooled me before, so I knew you needed help. We both ran to get the men." Earnestly he went on, "Drums heard in the forest at night always mean bad trouble." Then Watam ·noticed a sheepish look on Zeke's face. "They can mean trouble in the daytime, too," he added. "But Indian drums are never used for playing tricks."

Pony Express Horse

Jerry King rode his pony, Buster, down the trail to the place where a new building was going up. Approaching a red-bearded man, Jerry asked, "What are you building?"

"It will be the Pony Express station," the man replied. "The country is getting so big that we must have a faster way to carry the mail. Stagecoaches are too slow.

"An Express rider at St. Joseph, Missouri, will put letters in his mail pouch and gallop westward. He'll change horses every twenty miles until he has covered a hundred miles. Then he will hand the mail to a fresh rider, who will go a hundred miles farther. We'll keep spare horses here for the riders."

From: *Jerry and the Pony Express*, by Sanford Tousey. Copyright 1936 by Sanford Tousey, reprinted by permission of the author and Doubleday & Company, Inc.

"Will the Pony Express go all the way to California where my uncle is?" asked Jerry.

"Yes," said the man. "And other riders will come eastward from California. Rain or shine, heat or blizzard, they'll give the nation a faster mail service than ever before."

"Will there be many horses?" Jerry asked.

"Not so many here in eastern Kansas," said Red. "But along the trail there will be four hundred horses in all, and eighty riders. To get across two thousand miles of country quickly, all the horses must be very fast."

Every day after that Jerry rode down to watch the men at work. Before long they had constructed a log stable and a corral. Then they built the station house itself.

One day in late March, Jerry rode down to the station. There he saw some cowboys driving a band of horses into the corral.

"These are the horses that will run on the Pony Express Trail," Red told Jerry. "Aren't they beauties! The company paid as high as two hundred dollars for some of them."

"Maybe I will get to be a Pony Express rider when I grow up," Jerry said hopefully.

"Good boy!" said Red. "By the way you ride now, you'll make a good Express rider."

The first Express rider from Missouri was expected early in April. On the day that the rider was due, Jerry eagerly accompanied his father and the ranch hands to the station.

Jerry rode up to the top of a bluff. From here his keen eyes could see far down the trail. Soon he was rewarded. A tiny shape appeared on the horizon and grew larger and larger as it approached. Quickly Jerry dug his heels into Buster's sides and dashed back to the station, yelling, "Here he comes!"

George Towne, the Pony Express rider, came in at a full gallop and threw himself off his weary horse.

In a flash George transferred his *mochila* with its mail to a fresh horse. Then, scarcely touching the stirrup, he leaped into the saddle. As he galloped off on the next stretch of his hundred-mile run, the cowboys cheered wildly.

George's skill inspired Jerry to practice until he could make just such a getaway on Buster. The horse enjoyed the new game. Soon Jerry was showing all the ranch hands how Pony Express riders arrived and left.

"That boy will be carrying the mail one of these days," remarked one of the men.

During the summer and fall months Jerry often rode Buster out to meet George Towne. The boy would gallop alongside as the rider approached the station on a tired horse.

As the two rode along, Jerry would admire George's buckskin jacket, his horse, and his guns. George would grin, and often he would tell Jerry bits of news from along the trail.

One morning when Jerry was out riding on Buster, a strange sight met his eyes. A great wagon loaded with long wooden poles came past. As horses tugged it slowly along, the men on the wagon dropped a pole off onto the ground every few rods.

At home Jerry told what he had seen.

"Those are telegraph poles," Mr. King told his son, "Later, men will dig holes, set the poles in the ground, and stretch wires from pole to pole. Very soon this nation will have its first telegraph line from coast to coast. A telegraphed message travels much faster than one sent by Pony Express."

"But I'm going to be an Express rider!" Jerry said.

"I'm afraid not, Son," Mr. King replied. "By the time you're old enough for the job, there won't be any Pony Express."

Jerry was troubled. Could it be that his dream would never come true?

Early the next morning Jerry rode Buster down to the Pony Express station. There another strange sight greeted his eyes. Not a man nor a horse was to be seen!

"What has happened?" Jerry asked himself. "Where is everyone?"

Suddenly the boy heard hoofbeats. In a few minutes a rider galloped into the station yard. It was George Towne on his regular run. Immediately Jerry told him that there were no horses at the station.

George knew at once what had happened. "This is no surprise to me," he said. "For a long time some thieves in this region have been after the company's horses. Probably they stole the horses last night, and our men are out tracking them down.

"I don't know what to do now," continued George. "My horse is so tired out I don't think he can make it to the next station."

Jerry saw that George was eying Buster. The boy hesitated for just a moment.

"You can take my horse," Jerry offered, though his voice choked a bit.

"Thank you, son," said George.

An instant after transferring his saddle and
mail to Buster, George was astride the pony.
Then, thanking Jerry, he was off in a flash.

Jerry rode the tired Express horse home.
Several days later a man from the Pony
Express Company rode up to the King ranch
leading Buster. "Hello," the rider called out
to Jerry. "Here's the horse you lent George
Towne. He asked me to tell you that he had
to ride hard on his last stretch. Your pony
did his duty, but he was winded and will have
to take it easy for a while."

Jerry was glad to see Buster again. He
knew that he might never become an Express
rider. But it was almost as good to have a
horse that had worked for the Pony Express!

Bob Becomes a Railroad Man

When Number 23, the work train, arrived in Benton, Wyoming, Bob Barton was waiting to meet his father. Mr. Barton came home on weekends, and Bob always met him. The boy felt proud that his father was working on the first railroad to cross the United States.

To Bob, this railroad was the most exciting thing in the world. Two companies were in a race to finish it. Mr. Barton was in charge of laying rails west from Nebraska for one company. The other company was working eastward from the Pacific Coast. The union of the tracks was to take place in Utah.

As the railroad moved ahead, Bob and his mother moved, too. The closer Bob could be to the end of the track, the happier he was.

From: *Bob and the Railroad*, by Sanford Tousey. Copyright 1941 by Sanford Tousey reprinted by permission of the author and Doubleday & Company, Inc.

In fact, he hoped that someday he could bunk with his father in one of the freight cars at the railroad camp. These cars moved forward each day onto newly laid track, and the spot where they stood was called End o' Tracks.

On the way home that night Bob asked his father, "May I go to End o' Tracks with you Monday morning? Maybe I could get a job."

"Well," replied his father, "Mr. Casey, the foreman, does need a water boy. I guess I could take you with me. If you get the job, you can sleep in my bunk room."

On Monday Bob was up at daybreak. Hi King, the engineer of the work train, greeted him fondly. Bob's great desire was to be an engineer like Hi King. "Someday I'll control a big engine like this one," he thought.

Upon reaching the railroad camp, Bob was fascinated by the speed with which the men worked. Track-layers followed close behind men who leveled off the ground. Strong men threw wooden ties from horse-drawn wagons standing nearby. Tie-carriers then took the ties to the track and dropped them into place in rapid succession.

Next came a flatcar loaded with steel rails. It was pulled by a large horse. When the horse stopped, two groups of men—five on each side—stepped up to the flatcar. Each group grabbed a rail, placed it upon the ties, and spiked it, using heavy sledge hammers. Then the flatcar was pulled forward a rail's length, and two more rails were laid. Other men, following the car, packed down the earth between the ties.

When the flatcar was empty, it was quickly tipped on its side to allow another loaded car to pass it. Then the empty car was shoved back on the track and returned for more rails.

"The men work like lightning!" cried Bob.

"Yes, we don't want that other company to beat us to Utah," said Mr. Barton, grinning.

While Bob and his father were talking, Tim came up to them. Tim, the boy who drove the big horse that pulled the rail flatcar, had noticed Bob's interest. "Want to drive this load?" he asked. "May he, Mr. Barton?"

"Certainly," replied Mr. Barton, "if he'll do it as fast as you do."

Eagerly Bob took the reins from Tim and yelled "Get up!" to the big horse. Instantly it was off down the tracks. Bob followed as fast as he could. When the load of rails was delivered, he gave the reins back to Tim.

All day Bob dashed about watching the men at work. By evening he was exhausted, and soon after supper he rolled into his bunk.

The next morning Bob started his job as a water boy. Mr. Casey, the foreman, was a man of few words. He handed Bob a bucket and a dipper and said, "Get going!"

Hour after hour Bob trudged up and down the line of thirsty men with the water bucket. His arms ached long before quitting time.

On the third day, just as Bob was starting to get used to the work, the foreman came up to him. "Bob," he said, "Tim's foot was stepped on by the horse. He says that you drove all right the other day, so while Tim's foot is healing, would you drive the horse? Someone else will take over your job."

"Yes, sir," replied Bob, glad to drop the heavy water bucket.

The horse knew its job so well that it did not need much guiding. But Bob found the job harder than carrying water. It was run, run, all day long as he followed the big horse that pulled the flatcar loaded with rails.

"Had enough of railroading?" Bob's father laughingly asked that night.

"No, sir," answered Bob. "I'm going to learn *all* about it. I want to be an engineer and wear a cap like Hi King's."

In a few days Tim's foot had healed, and he and Bob were both back at their regular jobs. The two boys were soon great friends. Often they went off by themselves to sit and discuss their dreams of becoming engineers.

One moonlight night the boys were sitting near a clump of bushes. Suddenly they saw slinking in their direction the dim figures of two men. Their stealthy manner caused the boys to be suspicious. Quickly wriggling into the bushes, Bob and Tim watched the men.

The strangers hurried to a solitary pine tree, only twenty feet from where the boys were sitting. There they stopped.

"I put them right here," said the taller of the two men. He reached into some bushes near the tree. "Here they are," he said.

In the moonlight the boys saw a crowbar, a pickax, and other implements used by railroad men. There was also a gunny sack.

"Let's hurry with the job," said the other man. "Pulling spikes is no joke."

Bob whispered to Tim, "Let's follow them." Creeping along in Indian fashion one behind the other, Bob and Tim trailed the men.

A mile east on a hillside the strangers dropped their tools by the track. The boys stopped, too, and hid behind some bushes.

"This place is as good as any to start," said the tall man. Picking up the pickax and crowbar, the men set to work. Before long they had removed the spikes from two rails, muffling the noise with the gunny sack.

"When the early morning work train hits these rails," the tall man laughed wickedly, "it'll have to wait for a few repairs."

Trembling with excitement, Bob and Tim raced back to camp. There they reported the events they had seen to Mr. Barton.

"This is not the first time that men from the other company have damaged our track," he said. "They want to delay us so that their workmen will reach Utah first."

Mr. Barton and a few of his best workmen rushed to the hillside with sledge hammers and spikes. The damage was soon repaired.

Before Bob fell asleep that night, his father said to him laughingly, "You're going up fast, young man. At first you were a water boy, then a driver, and now you're a detective."

"But I would rather be an engineer like Hi King and wear a cap with a visor like his," Bob yawned.

Time went fast for Bob. Amazingly soon it was May 10, 1869. At breakfast Mr. Barton explained, "The last rail of each track goes down today. Officials of both companies will come out to Promontory Point to see the final spike driven in where the tracks meet. That spike is made of solid gold. But it's none too good for this important occasion."

As Bob and his father were about to board Number 23 that morning, Hi King called to Bob, "Come up in the cab with me. On my last trip to Omaha, I bought you something."

Raising the lid of his seat box, the engineer lifted out a new cap just like his own. On a polished brass plate above the leather visor appeared the words *Union Pacific Railroad.*

Bob's eyes sparkled. This cap would tell the world that Bob was a railroad man!

"We've all worked hard for this day," said Hi. "And you've worked as hard as anyone. So how would you like to operate something besides a water bucket, for a change?"

In a flash Bob was in the engineer's seat, ready to follow Hi King's directions.

"Toot the whistle, and put your hand on the throttle," Hi said. Bob felt Number 23 throb, and his heart throbbed with it. They reached Promontory Point all too soon. Then Hi took over and switched the engine to a siding.

Joining Mr. Barton and other men getting off the work train, Bob and Hi walked to the end of the main track. There the celebration was to be held.

After the band played, some speeches were made. Then there was complete silence so people could hear the taps of the big hammer on the golden spike. Everyone listened as those taps united the country by railroad from coast to coast.

Instantly the word *Done!* was telegraphed to great cities of the nation. Cannons were fired in many places, and the whole country celebrated the union of the tracks.

Then Bob told his father again, "I'd rather be a railroad man than anything else in the world!" And he meant it more than ever.

Wonders
of Today

The Great Idea

Joyce Warren knelt beside her big brother, who was sprawled underneath a leafy maple tree. "Lazybones!" she cried. "Aren't you going to do a *thing* to get ready for school? The first of September is next week. School starts September sixth. I've been working like a beaver helping get my clothes ready."

Ray yawned. "Well, Miss Pigtails," he said, "I can't shear lambs to get the wool for my pants. I can't knit my socks or sew my shirts. What do you suggest I do?"

"You could at least paint Red Arrow," said Joyce, eying Ray's ancient car standing in the gravel driveway. "It looks more like a wreck than any sort of automobile."

"Arrow's a bit scratched and rusty," Ray drawled. "But ugh! Painting! Horrible idea for such hot weather. I'd have to mix paint and find brushes. I'd have to spend hours and hours painting. Then I'd have to clean the brushes. The job would take days, and I'm quite content here in the shade."

Joyce looked disgusted. "It might take days if you painted with brushes," she said. "But you don't have to paint that old-fashioned way. You could paint Red Arrow with the new vacuum cleaner Mama got for her birthday. You'd know about that if you weren't always so careful never to have anything to do with *women's* work."

Joyce suddenly sprang up and raced across the lawn, leaving her brother speechless and bewildered by her words. In a few minutes she was back with the printed folder that had come with the vacuum cleaner.

"See," she said. "Here are pictures of all the things you can attach. One is a sprayer. You can use it to squirt ant-killer."

Ray had been acting interested. But now he was overcome with amusement. "I don't deny that my old gas buggy may have a few bugs. But spraying with ant-killer won't get rid of them," he said with a chuckle.

"The book says you can also spray *paint*," Joyce proceeded to tell her brother.

"It does!" exclaimed Ray, understanding at last what his sister had in mind. "That's a great idea, Joyce. There's only one possible catch to it. Will Mother let me borrow her brand-new vacuum for painting?"

"I'll ask while you get some paint," Joyce said, "if you'll promise to let me help paint."

"Sure, sure!" Ray replied with a clownish grin. "I'll permit that. After all, running a sweeper is a *woman's* task."

Ray and Joyce soon met again in the yard. He had several partly used cans of paint, a gunny sack and some rags, and a gallon pail. She was carrying the vacuum cleaner and the big awkward box of attachments.

"Mama said we'd have to clean the sprayer afterwards," puffed Joyce. "And we're not supposed to paint here in the yard. Where would be a good place for us to paint?"

"H-m!" Ray murmured thoughtfully. "Let's be sensible about this and pick a cool, shady location. Also we have to have electricity to run the sweeper. Let's set up shop near the barn—on the apple-orchard side."

Quickly they dumped the collection of cans and rags, the sweeper, and the attachments into the car and hopped in themselves. Then off they went in the ancient vehicle, jiggling and jerking toward the barn. After Ray had parked the car in the cool shadow of the big building, he and Joyce scrambled out and piled everything on the ground.

Joyce patted one of Arrow's rusty fenders. "Soon," she laughed, "this tin Lizzie will look like a dazzling royal coach fit for a queen."

Squatting on the ground, Joyce looked at the folder that explained how to fit the parts of the sprayer attachment together.

In the meantime Ray pulled the sweeper cord into the barn and attached it inside the room where Mr. Warren kept various farm implements. Then he came out and studied the directions for using the sprayer.

Soon Ray began to pour red paint into the glass paint container.

"Joyce," said Ray, "maybe *I* ought to try painting with the sprayer first. As soon as I see how it works, you may use it."

"All right," Joyce agreed. "I'll stay by the vacuum and turn it on and off when you tell me to. I'll be the switch operator."

Ray walked around between the barn and the car and aimed the sprayer at Arrow's left front fender. Joyce stood with her finger on the switch, waiting for Ray's signal.

"Let's begin!" he said with determination.

Click went the switch. The vacuum buzzed like bees swarming from a hive. Out of the sprayer swished a mist of scarlet paint.

Presently Ray yelled, "Turn it off!"

Joyce clicked the switch. "What's wrong?" she asked. "Won't the paint stick?"

"It sticks all right," Ray reported with a frown. "That's the trouble. It sticks where it shouldn't. There's as much paint on the headlight as there is on the fender. I was a simpleton not to realize that would happen. But I know how to solve the problem. We'll need some newspapers and some tape."

"I'll ask Mama for some papers and the sticking tape," cried Joyce, dashing away.

The pair worked unceasingly for an hour, putting strips of paper over everything on the car that was not to be painted. At last Ray gave the signal to turn on the vacuum again.

He had covered the surface of the left side of the car with glossy red paint and Joyce had finished painting the back section when Mrs. Warren rang the bell for lunch.

Ray and Joyce wasted no time in getting to the house. At the table the two feasted on ham sandwiches and slices of juicy peach pie topped with scoops of ice cream. Then they hurried back to the barn to continue painting.

Ray surveyed the job and announced, "I think we'd better paint the top next. Since neither one of us is a giraffe, I'll have to fix something to stand on. You put more paint in the jar while I find something."

By the time Joyce had refilled the jar, Ray had fetched two big bales of hay from the loft. He placed a wide plank across them, making a raised platform at the rear of the car.

"Up you go, Pigtails," he said. "You can paint the back section of the top. Tell me when you want the vacuum turned on."

At Joyce's signal, Ray clicked the switch. Then Joyce began spraying the paint—up and down, across and back.

Later, Ray painted the front section of the top and the hood of the car. Then together he and Joyce painted the right side. When they finished painting, it was almost dark.

Ray praised his sister. "Your idea was great," he said. "The painting is all done in one day, and the car looks fine. We'll leave it here tonight. By morning the paint will be dry. Then we'll ask the folks to take a look."

After breakfast the next day Ray and Joyce raced out to get Arrow ready for the grand showing. They had just removed the last bit of newspaper and tape and Ray had seated himself proudly in the front seat when both his parents came around the corner of the barn.

"Gracious! Why, old Arrow glitters like a jewel!" Mrs. Warren cried approvingly.

Ray said, "I'll back away from the barn so you can get a good look all around."

As Ray stopped the car and hopped out, he noticed that his parents were laughing.

"What's so funny?" asked Ray, joining the others. "Did we miss some spots?"

"Oh, no!" exclaimed Mr. Warren. "You covered everything. Even part of the barn!"

Both Joyce and Ray stared at the barn in shocked surprise. There on the boards was the unmistakable outline of a car.

"Oh, Papa!" gasped Joyce. "I—I'll take the blame for the damage. The idea of painting Arrow with the vacuum cleaner was mine."

"I'm not blaming anyone," Mr. Warren chuckled. "I've been hoping to get the barn painted this summer. Since you kids have started the job, you can finish it for me."

Ray said quickly, "I picked the location. So I should paint the barn." Then grinning comically, he added, "But in the future I'm going back to leaving women's work alone."

On with the Show

A bright blue station wagon was spinning along Lake Shore Drive amid heavy traffic. Cars in two lanes sped north. Those in six other lanes whizzed south. The blue car was southbound, headed for a television studio near Chicago's Loop. In the car were Mrs. Cannon, her eldest daughter, and her son.

Peter Cannon was gazing intently into the rearview mirror. He was studying a bruise he had received in football practice.

"I bet a fellow with a black eye can't be on TV," Peter ventured nervously.

"Gracious sakes!" cried his sister Betty. "Of course he can. Program directors who invite fifth-grade boys to be on TV have to expect them to be bruised and banged up."

172

Peter had been a winner in the Children's Book Week contest. He had been chosen to appear on a national television broadcast with Abe Darner, his favorite author.

Mr. Darner wrote many different kinds of books. A book that Peter liked particularly was a true war story about army doctors and nurses who flew to the battlefields to care for wounded soldiers. Another book was about diamond thieves. The hijackers were caught by the stewardess and the copilot on a plane. Mr. Darner's newest book was *Tales of My Tribe.* It was about boys of Peter's age.

Mrs. Cannon drove steadily on toward the Loop. Peter kept thinking about the famous author and the coming broadcast. The more he thought, the more worried he became.

Suddenly Peter said anxiously, "I wonder what we kids will have to do on the show."

Betty giggled, "It's called 'Book Talk.' So you'll probably talk about books." Then, to encourage her brother, she added soberly, "That'll be easy for a bookworm like you."

Peter groaned. "I wish I thought so."

"I know you're nervous, Son, but you don't need to be," said Mrs. Cannon with sympathy. "Mrs. French, who helps you at the library, will be there. You'll feel at home with her."

Just then a front wheel started making a rumbling noise, and the car began to sway.

"Oh, dear!" moaned Mrs. Cannon. "A flat tire and no spare! Besides, I can't stop in this traffic. I'll have to keep driving to the nearest emergency parking space."

On went the car—bumpety, thump, bumpety, thump. At the nearest emergency aid station Mrs. Cannon parked and got out. "The tire is as flat as a pancake," she announced.

Peter sighed and relaxed in the car seat. He felt both relief and disappointment. He would not have to be on TV after all. The delay would make him too late for the show.

All at once Peter saw his mother wave her arm. Immediately a taxicab pulled in behind them in the safety parking space.

"Hop into this cab," Mrs. Cannon said to Peter, "and go on to the studio."

The boy looked stunned. "You mean a— a—alone?" he faltered.

"No, Betty will go," Mrs. Cannon replied. "I'll have to remain here till a traffic officer comes along to call a garage for me."

Peter wailed, "I haven't thought of what to say!" His concern over the coming program made his voice shrill.

"I'll help you think," said Betty calmly as she hustled her brother toward the cab.

Mrs. Cannon smiled and patted her son's shoulder. "I have a suggestion," she said. "Ask the author whether he has a hobby."

To Peter it seemed only seconds until the taxi stopped in front of a tall building. The doorman told Betty and Peter how to get to the studio. Then Peter trudged miserably behind his sister to an elevator. They were whisked upward. And in no time at all Betty was opening a door marked *Studio A.*

Peter stepped cautiously into a huge room. He blinked in bewilderment at all the things he saw on the immense studio floor.

There were microphones hanging from big poles like bait on fishing lines.

There were three stage sets, one for a street scene, one for a modern kitchen, and one arranged with living-room furniture.

There were people everywhere—crews of cameramen and assistants, microphone men, television performers.

And big overhead lamps and spotlights were arranged to bathe everything in light.

Mrs. French noticed Peter's arrival. Her navy blue silk dress rustled cheerfully as she hurried to greet her young friend.

Betty left to sit in the studio audience with the other visitors. Mrs. French led Peter to the living-room stage set. She introduced the excited boy to a youthful man who turned out to be Mr. Darner and then to the three other children who were to be on "Book Talk."

Mrs. French said, "We've been rehearsing. We aren't saying exactly what we'll say later. But microphone men are adjusting the microphones. And the camera crew are focusing the cameras. They're rehearsing how they'll shoot some of the pictures."

Peter just nodded. His tongue seemed to be glued to the roof of his mouth, so that he could not utter a sound.

Mrs. French went on talking. "Mr. Darner has been answering some questions. He's told us that he has four sons. His home is at Cypress Cove. He has a kind of blossoming tree in his yard that none of us have ever seen. It's a tupelo tree. Now then, Peter, have you a question to ask?"

Peter's mind was a blank. He moistened his dry lips and silently wagged his head.

A girl spoke quickly. "I do. Mr. Darner, did all the funny things that you wrote about in *Tales of My Tribe* really happen?"

"Yes, they did," said Mr. Darner. "You recall that I mentioned having four sons. With four boys and their friends around the house, a lot of amusing things happen."

Another girl piped up, "Do your boys really have a pet skunk?"

"Not one pet skunk," laughed Mr. Darner, "a *family* of skunks. In fact, my boys have both a zoo and a museum of natural history. They have a sleepy old donkey and a goat that butts people all the time. They have a tame opossum. They have pigeons and barn owls, white mice and rats, frogs and snakes, raccoons and chipmunks. They even have a porcupine, but he's stuffed, thank goodness."

As the others chatted, Peter relaxed a bit and looked with curiosity around the stage set. He discovered a wee microphone hidden on a table behind some books and another tucked in a bowl of lilies.

Soon the floor manager approached. "Your show will commence in just ten minutes," he advised the group. "The director reports from the control room that everything's fine. Any questions before show time?"

"Yes," Peter ventured. "What are those fellows doing? And what are their machines called?" He pointed to a man operating the microphone that hovered near Mr. Darner's head and then to a man who was wheeling a cameraman about on a platform.

"That high stand with a pole attached to it is a microphone boom," said the floor boss. "As you see, a microphone hangs from the long pole. The boom operator makes the microphone follow a performer as he moves around on the stage. He turns a crank to extend the pole, and he swings it from side to side. He has to be careful never to let the microphone show in a picture."

Pointing to the camera outfit, the manager continued, "The low-wheeled frame at the bottom is called a dolly. The upper part to which the camera is attached is a crane. The cameraman perches on the crane and peers through his camera. The assistant pushes the dolly around. He also raises or lowers the camera and cameraman or moves them from side to side. He helps get close-ups and other interesting shots."

"Close-ups!" cried Peter, clapping a hand over his black eye. "Not of this, I hope!"

"The bruise won't show," the man said. "We'll just make up your face and disguise it. Come with me. The rest of the cast were made up before they started rehearsing."

The show began on the stroke of eleven. Peter felt as if he were in a foggy dream. He heard musicians play soft music. He heard Mrs. French introduce the author. He heard the other children ask questions. But it all sounded subdued and far away.

Just at the moment when it was Peter's turn to speak, he seemed to wake up. He remembered his question. "Do you have a hobby, Mr. Darner?" he asked clearly.

"Yes, I have," said the author. He pulled out a mouth organ and played a few bars of "Turkey in the Straw," then a few measures of "Oh! Susanna."

"Sing," he said to Peter.
So Peter sang.

As Mr. Darner was playing and
tapping his foot and Peter was singing
light-heartedly, Peter suddenly thought,
"Why, I'm singing! I've been talking and
now I'm singing on a national hookup. I wish
Mother were seeing this."

What Peter did not know was that his
mother *was* seeing the program. Her car
had been towed to a garage. Fortunately
for her, the garage had a television set. The
garageman had turned on the "Book Talk"
show for Mrs. Cannon. She had heard her
son's question. Now she was nodding her
head in time to Peter's gay singing.

Uncle Lem's Egg Beater

When Dad went fishing in Canada last year, he took my friend Phil and me along. We got off the train at Leaping Falls. Uncle Lem was at the station to meet us.

Uncle noticed right away the new chamois jacket Dad was wearing. "Say, Henry!" he exclaimed. "That's a mighty fine garment."

Dad agreed proudly, "It certainly is. It's a good one, too. It's light, but it's warm. And chamois keeps out wind and water."

As the men talked, they watched our bags and rod cases being unloaded. "What's that?" Uncle Lem asked, pointing to a long object.

"A canoe," Dad replied. Then he rushed to a baggageman who was about to toss out a package. "Don't throw that box. Hand it to me," he said.

Dad rushed back to Uncle Lem, who was staring in bewilderment. "Why, Henry," Uncle began, "I've got plenty of canoes."

But Dad interrupted him. "Not that kind, you haven't. That's an aluminum canoe. And here's an outboard motor to go with it."

While he spoke, Dad opened the box and showed a gleaming motor. It was one of the new models, easy to operate and light enough to carry without much effort.

We all expected Uncle Lem to think it was a marvel. Instead he looked disgusted. "Do you call that a motor?" he asked scornfully. "Looks like an egg beater. What good is it?"

Dad looked astonished. "What good is it!" he exclaimed. "I'll tell you what good it is."

Then he told how the motor could send a canoe racing through the water or keep it at slow speed. He kept bragging about the motor while we carried our things from the station down to the shore of Squaw Lake. But my stubborn uncle was not convinced.

"Still say it's an egg beater," he grunted.

We put our things aboard Uncle's old boat, tied the aluminum canoe on behind, and took off across the lake for Uncle Lem's cabin.

That night after supper we were all sitting around the fire. Phil and I were studying the directions that came with the motor. Dad was smoothing his new jacket. Uncle Lem was oiling his rifle and muttering to himself.

Finally he sputtered, "Motor for a canoe! There's no sense to it. Arms—human arms —were made long before machines!"

Dad was trying to watch his temper. "So were legs, Lem," he growled. "But you don't swim instead of riding in a boat."

"I could," my uncle mumbled. "Faster than that peanut-sized motor will take you."

Uncle Lem paused. Then he went on, "Do you remember that promontory on Roaring River where we camped last year and caught the bass? The mouth of the river is straight across the lake, about seven miles from here. The promontory is quite a distance upstream. All in all, it's about a day's canoe trip away."

Dad nodded his head.

"Well!" Uncle Lem cried. "I'll bet I can paddle a canoe there and back in less time than you can make the trip with that motor."

"What will you bet?" asked Dad.

"I'll put up my rifle against that fancy new garment of yours," Uncle Lem said firmly.

"It's a bet!" cried Dad. "We'll each take a passenger. First canoe back here wins."

"Fine!" exclaimed Uncle Lem. "You boys flip a coin to see who travels with me."

Phil and I flipped. I drew Uncle Lem.

Early the next day everyone was ready to go. "Now, Lem," Dad said, "remember to take only one paddle so Ed can't help you."

"All right," replied my uncle. "And don't you take *any*. You'll have to depend on that egg beater. All set, Henry? Let's go."

Uncle Lem paddled in a beeline toward the
river. But Dad's aluminum canoe shot past us
like a rocket. Uncle Lem said nothing. He
set his jaw and paddled harder.

My Uncle Lem is a born woodsman. He
paddled steadily all day. Finally at dusk we
reached the camp. Dad and Phil had already
chopped wood and built a couple of lean-tos
out of branches. Now they were squatting by
a fire, frying bass in a big iron skillet.

"Thought you two were lost," Dad called.

Uncle Lem just grunted, but I noticed that
he eyed the motor with respect.

Dad asked, "Want to call off the bet?"

"We aren't back yet," replied Uncle Lem.

We started home the next morning. Again Dad and Phil soon left Uncle Lem and me far behind. But much later, rounding a bend in the river, we saw Dad's canoe pulled up on a bank. Dad was kneeling over the motor.

As we landed close by, Uncle Lem called loudly, "Egg beater stopped beating?"

"Now, Lem!" Dad cried. "You can't blame the motor. I got water in the gasoline when I filled the tank. No engine on earth will run on watered fuel. Let's call the bet off."

"Oh, no!" exclaimed Uncle Lem. "That fancy jacket will look fine on me. Let me try it on." He began stripping off his coat. His tanned arms were bare to the elbow.

Dad would not remove the new jacket. So Uncle Lem, without his coat, went off to cut firewood. Before long we were eating bass and fried potatoes and onions. My uncle kept talking about how much better human bodies are than machines that break down.

Finally Phil noticed a rash on Uncle's right wrist and arm. "What's that?" he asked.

Glancing down, Uncle Lem said, "I must have touched some poison oak last night."

"Too bad, Lem," muttered Dad. "But what were you saying about machines getting out of order? Guess you forgot that people can, too. Now we'll call off our bet for sure."

Maybe it was the poison-oak rash that made Uncle Lem short-tempered. "Henry, I'm not thinking about the bet," he snapped. "I need to get home and take care of this arm. It's swelling. It's beginning to sting, too."

Uncle and I went to fasten Dad's canoe to ours so that we could tow it. As we worked, Uncle Lem groaned, "My shoulders are sore. I've been shoving too hard on that paddle."

Since traveling with the current would be easy, I offered to paddle for him.

Late in the afternoon we entered the lake. As we started across, a strong wind struck us. It was soon evident that a severe midsummer storm was coming up behind us.

"Ed, I'll paddle now," Uncle said to me.

He was an expert, but we saw that even his skill couldn't keep us ahead of the storm.

"Shouldn't we head for shore?" Dad called.

Uncle yelled, "Can't make it. We'll have to turn and face the wind. We're in for some trouble when that fifty-mile blast hits us."

We all knew what he meant. When the wind reached us, it would kick up waves six feet high. Our two canoes would be almost impossible to manage in those billows. And we had just one paddle among us.

Suddenly Phil called to Dad, "Let me have your jacket."

Dad looked amazed. "Why?" he shouted.

"I've an idea," Phil cried, "but I need your jacket. Hand me that bucket, too." As we stared at him, he added impatiently, "I'll strain the fuel through the jacket."

Our mouths dropped open in wonder and shame. All of us *knew* that chamois would strain water out of gasoline, but only Phil had remembered. Dad took one look at the rough waves. Then he peeled off his jacket and handed it over.

Phil stretched it over the pail. Carefully he poured the watered fuel from the tank through the chamois. Within a few moments he was pouring the strained gas back into the tank.

Dad set the motor in place and adjusted it. When he pulled the cord, the motor started.

Quickly we reversed the positions of the canoes so that Dad could tow Uncle Lem.

"Hang on!" Phil yelled as we whizzed off.

The little motor took us flying across the lake. We were ashore, dry and cozy in the cabin, when the storm hit.

After we had eaten our supper, my uncle
produced his rifle. He tried to look solemn,
but his eyes twinkled as he held the gun out
to Dad. "Take her," he said. "You won her
fair and square. That little egg beater is a
great invention. It saved our lives."

Dad beamed. "I don't want your rifle," he
answered. "All I wanted was to hear you
admit that you were wrong about machines.
If you'd like it, the outboard motor is yours.
I brought it up here as a gift for you."

Uncle Lem began to grin. "That's mighty
kind of you, Henry," he chuckled. "If you
keep on coming up here, I may get to be as
modern as that sweet little motor."

What's New?

Nick Weaver kept a pair of pliers in his back pocket and a great store of knowledge about modern machines in his head. Nick read about inventions in boys' magazines. He spent hours observing each new labor-saving machine that appeared in his small town.

To Nick, Mrs. Lent's sink that chewed up garbage was the best invention ever, until the village bank put in a new sidewalk. It was a heated one that melted snow and ice in winter. The new sidewalk made Nick very proud that his town was up-to-date.

The boy not only read about inventions. He frequently invented things. He had made a picture-frame radio for his father's den. For his own room he had made a weather guide.

With salt, cloth, nails, cardboard, and a wheel from a clock, he'd made a guide that smiled when the weather was sunny and frowned when it was stormy.

After a trip to Omaha with his grandfather, Nick stopped inventing. It was not that he had lost interest. He was just busy thinking about the finest invention he had seen yet.

Mr. Eagles and his grandson had gone to a store in Omaha to buy gifts—a necklace for Grandmother, slippers for Mother, elkskin driving gloves for Dad, a butterfly net for Nick's sister Holly. As the shoppers neared the door, it had opened all by itself.

Nick had stood spellbound. He had read about electric-eye doors. He knew that a beam of light shone across in front of the door and that when a person passed through the beam, the door opened itself electrically. Even so, a door that did not have to be pulled or pushed had enchanted Nick.

The day the travelers returned home, Nick did nothing but talk about Magic Eyes. Four times he asked his father about putting one on the garage. Four times his father refused.

"But think how up-to-date Cedar Point would be if we had even one Magic Eye in town!" Nick insisted.

Mr. Weaver said, "Get your tools out. Go invent something. You'll feel better." But Nick just sat, thinking about Magic Eyes.

On Monday, he had a talk with the school caretaker. "Mr. Wealthman," he said, "you need a Magic Eye on your broom closet."

"Nonsense!" exclaimed the man. "I can't think of anything I need less. Do you reckon I want you pupils running in and out of my closet all day to see a Magic Eye work!"

On Tuesday, the boy spoke to Miss Eve Coonen at the library. She doubted that the library would ever put in a Magic Eye. On Wednesday, he made an appeal to Mr. Ace Peppers at the gas station, with no success.

Nick was at his wit's end. "Some folks are satisfied to be old-fashioned," he thought bitterly. He considered speaking to the bank president, Mr. Burrows, and to Mr. Seeder, the county commissioner who had an office in town. Surely *they* believed in progress. But Nick lacked the nerve to do that.

On Thursday, Nick stopped at the village hardware store. There he often bought tacks, screws, electrical wire, and other things that he used for his inventions. He thought the hardware man would at least be interested in *talking* about Magic Eyes. And he was right. The two talked for a long time.

"If someone wanted to buy a Magic Eye, do you have one to sell?" Nick asked.

"No," said Mr. Vester. "But I could soon get one from Omaha or Kansas City."

On Friday, Nick had to go to Mr. Fulton's Grocery and Meat Market for his mother. The store had a very stubborn old door that seldom opened without sticking. When Nick pushed on the door, it stuck as usual.

Mrs. Banner was the only customer in the store when Nick entered. Old Mr. Fulton's grandson Philip was waiting on her. Her dog Midget was tied just inside the door. Nick noticed that Midget was wearing the latest thing in dog collars and blankets.

Mr. Fulton was sitting on a stool behind the counter arranging spices and puddings on a shelf. "Hello, my lad," he called out. "What's new in the inventing business?"

"Not much," answered Nick with a grin.

"Fiddlesticks!" cried Mr. Fulton. "As I recall, you've been tinkering with machines and inventing since you were five. There must be something new."

Gathering his nerve, Nick said, "I found out yesterday where you can get a Magic Eye door for your store—if you ever want one. Mr. Vester can order it from Omaha."

Mr. Fulton chuckled, "I don't believe I'm interested. It would probably cost a fortune."

"Magic Eyes may be expensive," agreed Nick. "But they are an excellent invention. One of them in Cedar Point would put our town on the map."

Just then Mrs. Banner started out of the store with a bag of groceries and her dog. The door was even more stubborn than usual. Before anyone could reach the door to help her with it, an awful thing happened.

As Mrs. Banner jerked on the door, the bag slipped. She clutched at it and tore it. Down rained groceries. They bounced on the floor, shaking it like a small earthquake.

Midget yipped and yelped and howled in fear. Luckily the only thing that hit the dog was a tomato, which squashed on his nose. But the floor was littered. Slices of bread and crumbs of what had been a coconut loaf cake were sprinkled among boxes of oatmeal and tea, a can of beets, and a cabbage head.

"You poor lambkin!" screeched Midget's enraged mistress as she picked up the dog. When she was quite sure that Midget was unharmed, she flew into a worse fury. Her face got purple, and she stuttered angrily, "There's—there's no excuse for this. It's a wonder poor Midget is still alive. A person would have to be a—an octopus to manage groceries *and* that old door of yours."

Poor Mr. Fulton tried to apologize. "I'm sorry, madam," he said most humbly. But Mrs. Banner did not hear him. She was storming, "I'll take my business elsewhere! I'll not come here again!" Then out she marched in a huff, leaving her groceries.

"What a misfortune!" sighed Mr. Fulton.

Later, as he was wrapping some meat for Nick, he gave the boy a wink. "You know, son," he said a little sorrowfully, "sometimes an expensive article is quite cheap after all. Sometimes it's a real bargain."

After that, Nick started hanging around the store every evening after school. One night Mr. Fulton told him to be sure to be at the store at opening time on Saturday.

When Nick arrived, Mr. Fulton was waiting outside. "Some folks thought I should be the one to test this door," he told Nick. "Some thought I should invite Mayor Valentine to walk through it first. But I said, 'It's Nick's door. He ought to give it its first trial.'"

Almost bursting with pride, Nick pranced through the only Magic Eye door in Cedar Point. The mayor was second. Lined up to be third was Mrs. Banner. On her face was a broad smile. You would never have guessed that she had once marched out of Mr. Fulton's store, vowing never to return.

All the Difference

The first Monday morning
after school was out, John
Service sat at the telephone,
calling one number after another.

When someone answered, he would say,
"This is John Service, Junior, at 103 West
Vine Street. I'd like very much to have the
job of mowing your lawn this week."

Sometimes the person at the other end of
the line asked, "Why?" Then he would say,
"My Scout troop is going camping at Acorn
Lake this weekend. We each have to earn
our own money to pay for the trip. I don't
have any camping equipment, so I want to
earn money for that, too."

As the morning hours ticked by, John lined
up a list of customers. He carefully typed a
work schedule and had just finished ruling the
paper when his father came home for lunch.
He put the schedule into his father's hand.

J. SERVICE'S MOWING SCHEDULE - MOWER PROVIDED MOWING TIME 2 hours a lawn. REST 15 minutes. RATE: One dollar a lawn.				
	8:00	10:15	1:15	3:30
Monday			Clam 102 W. Vine Paid:	Naysmith 116 W. Vine Paid:
Tuesday	Huddleston 113 W. Vine Paid:	Southern 121 W. Vine Paid:	Jones 24 N. 2nd Paid:	Shelly 34 N. 2nd Paid:
Wednesday	Armor 25 N. 1st Paid:	Innis 19 N. 1st Paid:	Quackenbush 21 S. 1st Paid:	Pina 39 S. 1st Paid:
Thursday	Cudworth 105 W. Dyer Paid:	Troller 108 W. Dyer Paid:	English 117 W. Dyer Paid:	Peddleson 122 W. Dyer Paid:
Friday	Spicer 125 W. Dyer Paid:	Wickman 26 S. 2nd Paid:	Saper 18 S. 2nd Paid:	

"See! I have lawns on Vine and Dyer Streets and on First and Second Avenues!" John exclaimed. "I've left space to write the pay. According to my arithmetic, I'll earn seventeen dollars. Camp costs seven. That leaves ten, more than enough for equipment."

This was Mr. Service's first knowledge of John's project. He was bewildered at first. But when John explained, Mr. Service was proud of his son. He wondered, however, whether John had not undertaken more work than he could possibly do in five days.

After lunch John took the family's ancient mower and went clattering across the street to Professor Clam's yard. He rolled up his sleeves, and at one-fifteen sharp he began the mowing. He cut the west half of the lawn quickly. But the ground slanted steeply down to a sidewalk at the eastern boundary of the yard. Mowing the slanting part took so long that John had no time to rest before going on to the Naysmiths' yard. Luckily it was level and could be mowed rapidly.

John got home in time to take a bath before dinner. After dinner he went to his room to record his day's earnings. At bedtime his father came up for a little conversation about lawn-mowing and to inspect the work record.

By eight o'clock Tuesday morning John was at work on Mr. Huddleston's smooth lawn. With almost no effort he sent the old mower skimming along. At nine-thirty the job was finished in record time.

Whistling gaily, John strolled to the corner drugstore for a coconut candy bar. Another Scout was a clerk in the drugstore. So John talked for a while before going back to work.

Grass-cutting in Mr. Southern's yard did not progress so well. The yard included a U-shaped rock garden that hindered the work. John had to trim the grass around the rock border with shears, being careful not to cut ferns and other plants growing there. That took an incredible amount of time. John was an hour behind schedule when he finished the job. But the yard looked very nice.

After eating a good lunch, John went on to his next job with renewed strength. When he wheeled the mower into Granny Jones' back yard, he discovered that the yard looked like a wilderness. The grass had not been cut all spring. Clumps of long-stemmed weeds dotted the expanse of tall grass.

John gave the old mower a shove into the grass. Immediately the machine stopped with a jolt. John yanked it in reverse and pushed again. On he went—shoving forward, tugging backward. After one mowing, the grass in the back yard was still ragged. John decided it looked as if it had been hacked off with a dull saw or gnawed off by an old witch with several teeth missing. He had to rake up the cut grass and weeds and mow a second time.

Mowing the front lawn did not take long. But when John finished, it was six o'clock. He was happy to have the extra money that Granny paid him. But he was worried, too, because he was a lawn behind schedule.

After dinner, in spite of his weariness, the boy trudged over to mow Mr. Shelly's yard. John was a husky lad, but at the completion of his day's work he was too exhausted to fill in his job record—or even to bathe. He fell into bed and was snoring the next minute.

On Wednesday, John woke to the steady drip of rain. Hoping it would not last long, he dressed quickly. But during breakfast the rain came pelting down in torrents.

"That does it," John said mournfully to his parents. "Even if the rain stops right away, the grass won't be dry enough to mow before tomorrow. Eleven lawns to do in two days! It's absolutely hopeless. What a greenhorn I was not to figure that it might rain!"

Mr. Service gave John a pat of sympathy as the boy left the breakfast table.

John kept busy all that day. He swept the attic for his mother, tinkered with his radio, read magazines, and patched his old buckskin moccasins. He also kept remembering the camping trip that he would not be taking.

That evening he and his dad discussed the whole disappointing matter. "I have to mow the neighbors' lawns," John declared, "even if it takes till Saturday night. I have to keep my agreements. A Scout keeps his word."

Suddenly his face brightened. "Say, Dad! I've an idea!" And he hurried on to explain.

"Very sensible!" his father cried. "The lawn-mowing project is all yours. But in this emergency, I'll help a bit. You get started early tomorrow. I'll call Ed Lasswell just as soon as the hardware store opens."

On Thursday, John awakened in a glare
of sunshine. He started mowing early and
was just finishing Mr. Armor's yard when his
father drove up and tooted the horn.

"Did you get it?" John called excitedly.

"It's in the trunk," answered his father.
"Mr. Lasswell was glad to rent you a power
mower. The rate is only a dollar a day, and
he says gas won't cost you much, either."

The two unloaded the mower. Then Mr.
Service poured gas through a funnel into the
fuel tank. Next he showed John how to wind
a stout rope around the starting spool.

"I'll stay with you until you've learned to
operate this machine," he assured his son.
He then motioned for him to yank the starting
rope. John gave a sharp tug, and the motor
began to purr—like a kitten, he thought.

Thursday afternoon and Friday, John was
the envy of all the boys for blocks around—
including some members of his Scout troop.
Admiring spectators stood on the sidewalk
and watched the buzzing mower. It seemed
to be pulling John after it as it raced over
lawn after lawn. Green plumes of cut grass
spouted out behind. The neighborhood dogs,
yipping joyously, romped after the machine.

When John was packing to go to the lake,
he said to his mother, "That power mower
and I did the impossible—cut eleven lawns in
two days! And I'm not a bit tired. A motor
surely makes all the difference."

S O S

A deep rumble of thunder died away in the distance. The lights in the second story of the old building flickered and then went off. Startled, Joseph Wren dropped the steering rods from a soapbox racer and glanced at the window. It was almost dark outside, and it was raining hard again. There had been a downpour every hour or two all day.

Throughout the afternoon, however, Joseph and Eddie Scott had not been conscious of the rain. Eddie had been tinkering with his racer. And Joseph had been practicing code signals, stopping only when the younger boy asked for help or advice.

"Well!" exclaimed Joseph. "Without lights, I can't see to do anything more. It must be late anyway. We'd better go home."

Eddie got to his feet and looked out at the pelting rain. "Wow! What a torrent! That's a lot of water for Illinois—even for Illinois in April. I wish we could stay here till it slacks up. But you're right. It is so dark that it must be after six. We'd better go."

Joseph shoved two dry cells, a telegraph key, and a homemade buzzer into a paper bag. "I'm going to take my buzzer set home tonight," he said. "I need more practice on that code. I know all the letters, but I get mixed up when I spell words."

In the swiftly gathering darkness, Eddie groped for his flashlight. Finding it at last, he pressed his thumb on the switch. A faint, unsteady light shone forth. "These batteries must be weak," he said as he moved toward the staircase that led to the first floor.

Eddie clattered briskly down the wooden stairs. Joseph followed. As Eddie reached the landing, he yelled back in surprise, "Hey, look down here! There's water all over!"

Joseph edged down beside Eddie. The glimmer of the flashlight showed the scene that had astonished Eddie.

Water was running several feet deep on the first floor. It hissed menacingly against boxes, barrels, and parts of second-hand cars. Now and then a rubber tire casing bumped against the stairs.

The front door had been left unlatched, and flood water from the creek nearby had forced it open. Now the two boys peered into the deepening dusk, searching hopefully for the familiar creek bank. They saw instead an expanse of swirling, mud-colored water.

Suddenly Joseph had visions of the building being washed away. Other buildings had once stood here by the creek about a quarter of a mile from town. But floods in years past had destroyed them. In this big old warehouse Mr. Scott stored auto parts that he had no room for in his garage in town. It was the only building left in the vicinity.

"We might wade," Joseph began. But his common sense warned him that *that* would be folly. The flood water outside was deep— too deep to try such a rash plan.

"We'll stay inside," Eddie declared firmly. "This building is some protection. At least we're dry."

"We're dry *now*," retorted Joseph as he extended his hand and took Eddie's flashlight. Then he focused its beam on the steps.

The water was rising fast. As the boys watched, flood water began to trickle over a step nearer the landing.

Eddie began to sense their plight. "Joe!" he cried in a shrill voice. "Water may rise to the second floor. Come on! Help me put my racer up on some boxes."

As the boys reached the top of the stairs, a flash of lightning lighted the whole second story. A deafening clap of thunder shook the building. Eddie jumped and accidentally hit Joseph's arm, knocking the flashlight to the floor. In the darkness Eddie spoke. "That was close," he said, trying hard to control his shaky voice. "I hate electrical storms."

Joseph found the flashlight and then tried the switch. "The bulb's burned out or broken," he explained soberly. "We can't see to move the racer. Let's have a look outside."

The boys felt their way across the floor to the window. Then Joseph began polishing the dusty glass with his fist. Anxiously he peered toward town. The electricity was off there, too. Joseph saw only a few candles or kerosene lamps glimmering.

At last he sighed and spoke. "I bet my mother is worried sick. After lunch I told her I was going to the library. Then I found a new code book and came here to practice."

"My folks aren't worried about me," Eddie said, gazing into the inky night. "They are in Lake Bluff, visiting my Uncle Amos and Aunt Clara. They aren't due back until late."

Just then lightning flashed, lighting the scene outside. Eddie saw that the warehouse was encircled by muddy flood water.

Shrinking from the window with a shudder, Eddie cried, "We're trapped! We can't get out of this place."

Joseph spoke quickly. "Don't lose your nerve. We'll get out. We'll think of a way."

As Eddie stood numb with fear, he heard the muffled drone of a plane high above the storm. "It's probably an army plane that's circling the airport for a landing," he said. "I wish it were landing to pick us up."

"Might as well wish it were a navy ship coming to rescue us," said Joseph gruffly.

"Could we—" Eddie faltered, "could we use that old tire casing for a boat? There must be something around here that would do for oars."

"Too heavy," Joseph growled. "The tire casing would sink before we got ten feet."

"If we had an inner tube!" moaned Eddie. "If we only had an inner tube to use for a life preserver! If Dad only kept tubes here!"

Just at that moment there was a series of blinding flashes of lightning. Eddie gasped, "We've got to get out of this place even if we have to swim."

Joseph retorted, "Current's too strong. It would wash us away like dry leaves."

Then Eddie voiced the unbearable thought that was in both their minds. "The current *could* wash this shack away with us inside. We've just *got* to get out!"

"All right," said Joseph. "At least we can climb the ladder to the roof. Come on."

Hand in hand they groped their way across the inky room. Halfway to the ladder they stumbled into Eddie's racer. Eddie lost his balance and sprawled on the floor. Joseph lurched forward, dropping his buzzer set.

Both boys groped for the various parts of the set. Just as they found the last one, the sound of a plane drew their attention again.

"Say, Joe!" Eddie cried excitedly. "You're a code expert. Can you send an S O S? The way planes do, I mean."

Joseph sat clutching his telegraph key. He began tapping it unconsciously. "Sure, I can send S O S," he said. "This is it." Then he tapped three shorts, three longs, and three more shorts. "But I have to have power."

"Use your dry cells," suggested Eddie.

Joseph only muttered. But the next time there was a flash of lightning, he started to connect the key and buzzer to the dry cells. Before long the buzzer set was connected. Then Joseph began tapping out the distress signal that is understood not only nationally but all over the world.

"There's not enough power here to do us any good," he said. "I can barely hear the buzz. I guess the batteries are worn out."

Eddie asked, "Can you use ordinary car batteries—storage batteries? My father has several old ones in a cupboard over here. I don't know what condition they're in."

Joseph followed Eddie to a wall cupboard. During a succession of lightning flashes they found seven batteries and various old tools, including pliers and a screwdriver.

Joseph experimented and found that the first battery was completely dead. The next one was weak, but it did spark.

Eddie asked, "Could you connect all the good ones? Once Dad hitched two storage batteries together to start our car. He said he increased the power that way."

"Where would I get wire to connect two or three batteries?" Joseph mumbled. "I'd need quite a bit."

Eddie did not answer.

Joseph heard slow, careful footsteps, an odd snap, then more steps. "Here's all the wire you can use," Eddie said. "I jerked it from that low ceiling light."

The darkness hindered Joseph's work. But fortunately lightning continued to flash now and then as the boy put connecting wires on three batteries. Joseph then connected the buzzer and the key to the storage batteries. When he touched the key, there was a burst of light and a strong buzzing sound.

Trembling with excitement, Joseph tapped the code signal for distress—three shorts in rapid and regular succession, three longs, and then three more shorts.

"Wow!" cried Eddie joyfully. "You have power enough now. Send another S O S."

Again Joseph started tapping the distress signal. Suddenly he stopped. In a subdued voice he said, "We might as well quit all this code stuff."

"Why?" asked Eddie. "We have power."

Joseph replied, "Yes, we have power. But we are lacking one very important piece of equipment. If you think for a minute, you'll know what it is."

Without giving Eddie time to think, Joseph continued bitterly, "We have power. We have a key to send signals. But what do we have to make sound that can be heard even a block away? Nothing! My buzzer can't be heard outside this building."

The two boys sat in stunned and miserable silence, thinking of their plight. They knew that the sheet of water outside was growing ever larger and more dangerous. In their despair they forgot that they had planned to escape by climbing to the roof. The sound of a motor high up in the air just then made them feel even more hopeless. Help was so near, yet so very far away.

Finally Eddie swallowed the lump in his throat. Falteringly he asked, "Could we— could we signal with a light? There is an old headlight from a car here. I thought I'd use it as an ornament on my racer. But I decided it would only add weight. Anyway, it may be against the rules. Could we use the headlight in some way?"

"We surely could!" Joseph cried. "We'll attach the headlight to the batteries. Then we can flash some light signals from the window. Maybe that pilot who's been circling around will see them."

In the darkness Joseph worked feverishly to attach the wires to the old headlight. Then he fastened the free ends of the wires to the storage batteries, and the headlight gleamed in the dark room.

"Now!" cried Joseph. "You hold the light against the window. I'll flash S O S."

Again and again the distress signal blinked from the window of the warehouse. All of a sudden, from his position near the batteries on the floor, Joseph spoke excitedly. "Eddie, is that droning sound coming nearer?"

Almost instantly Eddie shrieked, "I can see lights in the sky flashing an answer. What shall I do?"

"Try to read the signal!" Joseph ordered. "Call out the dots and dashes to me."

Somewhat uncertainly Eddie began. "Dot, dash, dash," he said and stopped. Then he went on. "Dot, dot, dot, dot; a single dot; dot, dash, dot; and another single dot."

At the same time Joseph was mumbling the letters of the alphabet that the dots and dashes stood for. "That spells *where*," he shouted. "The pilot sees our signals. Hold the light steady. I'll give our location."

With shaking hands he tapped the letters for *at creek* and *on warehouse*.

When the droning was almost overhead, Joseph yelled, "It's the army helicopter from the airport. I would know the sound of that propeller anywhere."

"It's the army helicopter all right," Eddie squealed. "And it's focusing a light on this building. We'll be saved, Joe! The pilot will throw out a rope or something and rescue us." As he spoke, Eddie was scrambling toward the ladder that led to the roof. "Come on, Joe!" he shouted.

By the time Joseph had climbed out on the roof, Eddie had already whipped off his shirt. He stood waving the garment in the light from the helicopter as the machine glided nearer to the roof of the building.

Soon the two boys were safely inside the hovering machine. "I saw your signals from above the airport," said Pilot Sales. "At first I thought someone was making a nuisance of himself. Then I decided the person was in real trouble. What were you signaling with?"

"A headlight," Joseph answered quickly. Then, together, the boys told the whole story of their adventure. "Even with the light, I was afraid that our signals wouldn't be understood," Joseph finished with a sigh.

"You needn't have worried," replied Pilot Sales. "You boys really know your code."

Joseph cried, "My code book! I forgot it! It'll be washed away with Eddie's racer."

Stephen Sales chuckled. "You don't need a book. Your signals were perfect. Besides, the rain's over. The flood water will soon go down. Your book and the racer are safe enough if they're on the top floor."

On the way home from the airport, Joseph said to Eddie, "Stop at my place. My mother will fix us a skilletful of ham and eggs and a pile of toast and jam a mile high. Being scared makes me hungry. How about you?"

Storyland of Here and Now

The Missing Bones Mystery

When Jerry the police dog invited Wally the bloodhound to lunch, there wasn't any. This could have proved embarrassing. But these two were old friends. They had both been on the police force for a long time.

Jerry yipped mournfully, "I buried some choice lamb chop bones for us here. But they're gone now!" Then he appealed to his friend, "Help me find them, will you, Wally?"

The bloodhound, who was a detective with years of experience, replied, "Oh, let it go. Why labor on our day off!" But Jerry was already absorbed in studying the ground.

Adapted, and reprinted by permission of David McKay Company, Inc., from *MIXUPS AND FIXUPS: New-fangled Animal Stories;* copyright, 1953, 1954, by Evelyn Weiss.

"Peculiar!" Jerry cried. "No footprints!"

Wally said, "Generally, in cases like this, there are scratchprints, too." He strode over to look for himself. "You're absolutely right. Not a trace of prints of any kind."

"Scent out the thief, Chief," Jerry urged.

Wally, true-blue detective that he was, saw his duty, and he undertook the case.

He flapped his floppy ears and wiggled his long snout. Then, widening his nostrils, he proceeded to sniff a time or two. He set his nose to the ground.

"I *smell* chop bones," Wally announced. "And if my expert nose knows anything, they have been gone from this vicinity less than an hour. When did you deposit them here?"

"Just one hour ago," Jerry assured him.

"Which means, therefore," added the wily bloodhound, "that somebody took the bones shortly afterwards. Which means that *that* somebody is a fast worker."

Finding no helpful clues by the hole, Wally raced hither and thither in frenzy. Then in a bass voice he barked out suddenly, "This way, Mate! I have the scent!"

227

As they raced off abreast, Jerry barked a bewildered bark. *"How* can the trail begin anywhere except at the hole?"

Wally said, "Don't know. But if the scent leads to the pond, as I've a hunch it does, this case will be a snap. Thieves believe that bloodhounds can't trail them over water. They get that idea from the movies."

The trail did lead to the little pond in the swamp. Wally waded in and swam around. Then he crawled up the slippery bank. "It's incredible," he said. "There's no scent."

Back at the hole, the two held a powwow. Wally growled, "It is evident that we shall have to take some scientific steps to get to the bottom of this case."

"I could make a list of clues," said Jerry.

"That's a sensible step!" Wally exclaimed.

"But I can write only first letters," Jerry apologized. "I know my alphabet, but I was never much at spelling."

"Just note the details," said
Wally. "Begin with C for *clues.*
Then put H for *hole.*" Jerry
drew the letters on the ground,
having nothing else handy.

"I'll put I for *impossible,*"
he said. "It's impossible to take bones away
without leaving a trail to somewhere."

"Put P for *pond,*" Wally continued. "Our
next step is to construct a very cunning trap.
We'll bury more bones in that hole."

"Whose bones?" Jerry asked suspiciously.

"Yours," said Wally. "You have others."

"Only my rainy-day savings!" cried Jerry.

Wally went on grandly, "I pledge you that
nothing—*nothing*—will happen to them. I'll
tie one end of a stout string to the bones
and tie the other end to my foot. When our
enemy attempts to steal the bones, we'll just
creep up stealthily and pounce on him!"

After very soberly considering Wally's plan, Jerry agreed to it. He went to fetch more bones while Wally sought string. They set the trap and hid in a thicket. Crouching on their haunches, they waited.

A long, wearisome hour passed.

Jerry's legs were numb. He wriggled this way, and he squirmed that way. Finally he could endure sitting and waiting no longer.

"I thought you said this fellow was a fast worker," he declared in a muffled voice.

"Hush!" Wally replied. "He hasn't begun yet. The string is still attached to my foot."

Peeping from the bushes to get a look at the hole, Jerry exclaimed, "Yes! But are the bones still on the string?" He twitched it to see. The string seemed slack.

Feverishly, Jerry began tugging the string. He yanked yards of it into the thicket where they sat. At last the end appeared. Lo and behold! It was bare of bones!

With an angry whoof, Jerry shot from the thicket like a rocket. He dug rapidly into the hole. "The bones! They—they're gone!" he sputtered in distress.

Tangled in string, Wally lurched clumsily toward the hole. "Jumping fishcakes!" he shouted in bewilderment. "The bones must have been taken when we turned our backs to go into the thicket. But we *are* making progress. Quick, Jerry! You must provide more bones!"

Jerry bristled. "No!" he cried. "I have risked too much already. We'll just drop the case."

"We'll not drop the case," disputed Wally. "Think of our reputation! Always finish what you commence, I say. Be a sport, Jerry. I'll repay you if your bones are lost."

So while Wally untangled himself, Jerry got more bones. They reset the trap and hid again. But they didn't turn their backs once.

Suddenly Jerry gulped. He pointed toward the hole. "Look! The hole! It's moving!" And it was—unmistakably. By slow stages the level of the earth over the hole was sinking.

Wally and Jerry inched toward it.

"Beware!" warned Jerry. "There may be a monster pushing up out of there."

Wally was watching with a scientific eye. "It isn't pushing *up*," he said, "but *down*."

The two hovered at a safe distance until the mysterious movements ceased. "Now," Wally said with determination, "let's get to the bottom of this case. We'll dig!"

The pair dug with frenzied haste. Soon they uncovered an underground tunnel.

"Someone dug from underneath and took the bones," said Wally. "There's no other scientific way to explain it. Write down the clues, Jerry. *Moving earth. Underground passage.*" Quickly Wally put his ear to the hole. *"Noises!* Get that, too."

Shakily Jerry wrote an M, a U, and an N.

Wally sniffed. "Is that chipmunk scent?"

"Come out of that tunnel with your hands up!" Jerry barked. "You're under arrest."

"Wait! Wait!" exclaimed Wally. "You've overlooked something. A chipmunk doesn't eat bones. So he'd have no use for them."

"True! It's unreasonable," Jerry admitted. "A chipmunk would never take bones—any more than a bear would take overcoats."

"Unreasonable!" screeched a shrill voice. "If a bear found his door blocked by a lot of overcoats, he'd leave them there, I suppose."

Wally yelled, "The key to the mystery, my boy! Get that down, Jerry." And Jerry put down a large K for *key*.

"Did you ever see a set of clues add up the way these do?" Jerry cried joyously.

Pronouncing the letters clearly, Wally read C-H-I-P-M-U-N-K. Then he yelled, "He's our man! You buried bones in his doorway, Jerry, so he moved them. I always say the deeper you dig, the nearer the truth you get."

"Don't dig any deeper, or I'll chew on your ears!" the aroused chipmunk snarled.

"But may I have my bones?" asked Jerry.

Plop! A bone popped out and landed with a thud on Jerry's nose. P-link, p-lip, p-lop! The rest of the bones in the third set came bouncing out in rapid succession.

"Thanks," Jerry called. "And I'm sorry about your doorway. It was covered with leaves. I didn't know anybody lived there."

The disagreeable chipmunk chattered in a nasty tone about people who break laws and don't receive punishment. He snarled about detectives who think they know everything.

Jerry apologized again and asked the bad-tempered animal for the rest of the bones.

"No!" the disagreeable chipmunk retorted.

"They were my rainy-day savings," Jerry explained. "Surely you wouldn't keep them."

"I haven't got them," snarled the chipmunk. "I can't give what I haven't got."

"Well, then," said Wally, "tell us where they are, and we'll get them ourselves."

The chipmunk replied saucily, "I won't tell where they are, but I'll give you a hint. Go fish for them."

Scowling, Wally repeated, "Fish for them! Read off those clues again, Jerry."

C-H-I-P read Jerry. "P is for *pond!*"

Then off he ran and hurled himself blindly into the water. Gl—ub, bl—ub came from the depths of the pond. Finally Jerry floundered to the top with a mouthful of bones.

As Jerry divided the bones into two equal piles for lunch, he remarked flatteringly, "That was fine detective work, Boss. But I still don't see how the chipmunk transferred the bones to the pond without leaving a trail back to his home."

"W—well," Wally stuttered. Then he said, "It was simple. One by one he dragged the bones along the tunnel and out another hole. Then he climbed a tree, ran out on a long limb, jumped down, and went to the pond."

"My! That chipmunk was pretty scientific, too," said Jerry. "But now, let's eat!"

How the Camel
Got His Hump

In the beginning of years, when the world was so new and all, and the Animals were just beginning to work for Man, there was a Camel, and he lived in the middle of a Howling Desert because he did not want to work; and besides, he was a Howler himself. So he ate sticks and thorns and milkweed and

236

From: *Just So Stories*, by Rudyard Kipling, reprinted by permission of Mrs. George Bambridge and Doubleday & Company, Inc., and of The Macmillan Company of Canada.

prickles, most 'scruciating idle; and when anybody spoke to him he said "Humph!" Just "Humph!" and no more.

Presently the Horse came to him on Monday mo₋ning, with a saddle on his back and a bit in his mouth, and said, "Camel, O Camel, come out and trot like the rest of us."

"Humph!" said the Camel; and the Horse went away and told the Man.

Presently the Dog came to him, with a stick in his mouth, and said, "Camel, O Camel, come and fetch and carry like the rest of us."

"Humph!" said the Camel; and the Dog went away and told the Man.

Presently the Ox came to him, with the yoke on his neck and said, "Camel, O Camel, come and plough like the rest of us."

"Humph!" said the Camel; and the Ox went away and told the Man.

At the end of the day the Man called the Horse and the Dog and the Ox together, and said, "Three, O Three, I'm very sorry for you (with the world so new-and-all); but that Humph-thing in the Desert can't work, or he would have been here by now, so I am going to leave him alone, and you must work doubletime to make up for it."

That made the Three very angry (with the world so new-and-all), and they held a palaver, and an *indaba*, and a *punchayet,* and a pow-wow on the edge of the Desert; and the Camel came chewing milkweed *most* 'scruciating idle, and laughed at them. Then he said "Humph!" and went away again.

Presently there came along the Djinn in charge of All Deserts, rolling in a cloud of dust (Djinns always travel that way because it is Magic), and he stopped to palaver and powwow with the Three.

"Djinn of all Deserts," said the Horse, "*is* it right for anyone to be idle, with the world so new-and-all?"

"Certainly not," said the Djinn.

"Well," said the Horse, "there's a thing in the middle of your Howling Desert (and he's a Howler himself) with a long neck and long legs, and he hasn't done a stroke of work since Monday morning. He won't trot."

"Whew!" said the Djinn, whistling, "that's my Camel, for all the gold in Arabia! What does he say about it?"

"He says 'Humph!'" said the Dog; "and he won't fetch and carry."

"Does he say anything else?"

"Only 'Humph!'; and he won't plough," said the Ox.

"Very good," said the Djinn. "I'll humph him if you will kindly wait a minute."

The Djinn rolled himself up in his dust-cloak, and took a bearing across the desert, and found the Camel—most 'scruciatingly idle, looking at his own reflection in a pool of water.

"My long and bubbling friend," said the Djinn, "what's this I hear of your doing no work, with the world so new-and-all?"

"Humph!" said the Camel.

The Djinn sat down, with his chin in his hand, and began to think a Great Magic, while the Camel looked at his own reflection in the pool of water.

"You've given the Three extra work ever since Monday morning, all on account of your 'scruciating idleness," said the Djinn; and he went on thinking Magics, with his chin in his hand.

"Humph!" said the Camel.

"I shouldn't say that again if I were you," said the Djinn; "you might say it once too often. Bubbles, I want you to work."

And the Camel said "Humph!" again; but no sooner had he said it than he saw his back, that he was so proud of, puffing up and puffing up into a great big lolloping humph.

"Do you see that?" said the Djinn. "That's your very own humph that you've brought upon your very own self by not working. To-day is Thursday, and you've done no work since Monday, when the work began. Now you are going to work."

"How can I," said the Camel, "with this humph on my back?"

"That's made a-purpose," said the Djinn, "all because you missed those three days. You will be able to work now for three days without eating, because you can live on your humph; and don't you ever say I never did anything for you. Come out of the Desert and go to the Three, and behave. Humph yourself!"

And the Camel humphed himself, humph and all, and went away to join the Three. And from that day to this the Camel always wears a humph (we call it "hump" now, not to hurt his feelings); but he has never yet caught up with the three days that he missed at the beginning of the world, and he has never yet learned how to behave.

Pooh and Piglet Go Hunting
and Nearly Catch a Woozle

The Piglet lived in a very grand house in the middle of a beech tree, and the beech tree was in the middle of the forest, and the Piglet lived in the middle of the house. Next to his house was a piece of broken board which had "TRESPASSERS W" on it. When Christopher Robin asked the Piglet what it meant, he said it was his grandfather's name, and had been in the family for a long time. Christopher Robin said you *couldn't* be called Trespassers W, and Piglet said yes, you could, because his grandfather was, and it was short for Trespassers Will, which was short for Trespassers William. And his grandfather had had two names in case he lost one—Trespassers after an uncle, and William after Trespassers.

"I've got two names," said Christopher Robin carelessly.

"Well, there you are—that proves it," said Piglet.

242

One fine winter's day when Piglet was brushing away the snow in front of his house, he happened to look up, and there was Winnie-the-Pooh. Pooh was walking round and round in a circle, thinking of something else, and when Piglet called to him, he just went on walking.

"Hallo!" said Piglet, "what are *you* doing?"

"Hunting," said Pooh.

"Hunting what?"

"Tracking something," said Winnie-the-Pooh very mysteriously.

"Tracking what?" said Piglet, coming closer.

"That's just what I ask myself. I ask myself, What?"

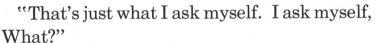

"What do you think you'll answer?"

"I shall have to wait until I catch up with it," said Winnie-the-Pooh. "Now, look there." He pointed to the ground in front of him. "What do you see there?"

"Tracks," said Piglet. "Paw marks." He gave a little squeak of excitement. "Oh, Pooh! Do you think it's a—a—a Woozle?"

"It may be," said Pooh. "Sometimes it is, and sometimes it isn't. You never can tell with paw marks."

With these few words he went on tracking, and Piglet, after watching him for a minute or two, ran after him. Winnie-the-Pooh had come to a sudden stop, and was bending over the tracks in a puzzled sort of way.

"What's the matter?" asked Piglet.

"It's a very funny thing," said Bear, "but there seem to be *two* animals now. This—whatever-it-was—has been joined by another —whatever-it-is—and the two of them are now proceeding in company. Would you mind coming with me, Piglet, in case they turn out to be Hostile Animals?"

Piglet scratched his ear in a nice sort of way, and said that he had nothing to do until Friday, and would be delighted to come, in case it really *was* a Woozle.

"You mean, in case it really is two Woozles," said Winnie-the-Pooh.

And Piglet said that anyhow he had nothing to do until Friday. So off they went together.

There was a small spinney of larch trees just here, and it seemed as if the two Woozles, if that is what they were, had been going round this spinney. So round this spinney went Pooh and Piglet after them, Piglet passing the time by telling Pooh what his Grandfather Trespassers W had done to remove Stiffness after Tracking, and how his

Grandfather Trespassers W had suffered in his later years from Shortness of Breath, and other matters of interest, and Pooh wondering what a Grandfather was like, and if perhaps this was Two Grandfathers they were after now, and if so, whether he would be allowed to take one home and keep it, and what Christopher Robin would say. And still the tracks went on in front of them. . . .

Suddenly Winnie-the-Pooh stopped, and pointed excitedly in front of him.

"Look!"

"What?" said Piglet, with a jump. And then, to show that he hadn't been frightened, he jumped up and down once or twice more in an exercising sort of way.

"The tracks!" said Pooh. *"A third animal has joined the other two!"*

"Pooh!" cried Piglet. "Do you think it is another Woozle?"

"No," said Pooh, "because it makes different marks. It is either Two Woozles and One, as it might be, Wizzle, or Two, as it might be, Wizzles and One, if so it is, Woozle. Let us continue to follow them."

So they went on, feeling a little anxious, in case the three animals in front of them were of Hostile Intent. And Piglet wished very much that his Grandfather T. W. were there, instead of elsewhere, and Pooh thought how nice it would be if they met Christopher Robin suddenly but quite accidentally, and only because he liked Christopher Robin so much. And then, all of a sudden, Winnie-the-Pooh stopped again and licked the tip of his nose in a cooling manner, for he was feeling more hot and anxious than ever in his life before. *There were four animals in front of them!*

"Do you see, Piglet? Look at their tracks! Three, as it were, Woozles, and One, as it was, Wizzle. *Another Woozle has joined them!*"

And so it seemed to be.

There were the tracks, crossing over each other here, getting muddled up with each other there—but quite plainly, every now and then, the tracks of four sets of paws.

"I *think*," said Piglet, when he had licked the tip of his nose, too, and found that it brought very little comfort, "I *think* that I have just remembered something. I have just remembered something that I forgot to do yesterday and shan't be able to do to-morrow. So I suppose I really ought to go back and do it now."

"We'll do it this afternoon, and I'll come with you," said Pooh.

"It isn't the sort of thing you can do in the afternoon," said Piglet quickly. "It's a very particular morning thing, that has to be done in the morning and, if possible, between the hours of— What would you say the time was?"

"About twelve," said Winnie-the-Pooh, looking at the sun.

"Between, as I was saying, the hours of twelve and twelve-five. So, really, dear old Pooh, if you'll excuse me— *What's that?*"

Pooh looked up at the sky, and then, as he heard the whistle again, he looked up into the branches of a big oak tree, and then he saw a friend of his.

"It's Christopher Robin," he said.

"Ah, then you'll be all right," said Piglet. "You'll be quite safe with *him*. Good-by." And he trotted off home as quickly as he could, very glad to be Out of All Danger again.

Christopher Robin came slowly down his tree.

"Silly old Bear," he said, "what *were* you doing? First you went round the spinney twice by yourself, and then Piglet ran after you and you went round again together, and then you were just going round a fourth time——"

"Wait a moment," said Winnie-the-Pooh, holding up his paw.

He sat down and thought, in the most thoughtful way he could think. Then he fitted his paw into one of the Tracks . . . and then he scratched his nose twice, and stood up.

"Yes," said Winnie-the-Pooh.

"I see now," said Winnie-the-Pooh.

"I have been Foolish and Deluded," said he, "and I am a Bear of No Brain at All."

"You're the Best Bear in All the World," said Christopher Robin soothingly.

"Am I?" said Pooh hopefully. And then he brightened up suddenly.

"Anyhow," he said, "it is nearly Luncheon Time."

So he went home for it.

Babe, the Blue Ox

Paul Bunyan was the mightiest logger that ever lived. But he couldn't have done half the work he did without Babe, his blue ox. Babe was the biggest ox in the world. When he was measured for a yoke, he was forty-two ax-handles between the eyes. He must have weighed thousands of tons, though he never was weighed, for no scales were big enough.

The tips of his horns were very far apart. A crow deciding to fly from one horn to the other in the dead of winter did not reach the other horn until after the spring thaw.

Babe's body was so long that Paul had to carry a pair of field glasses in order to see what the ox was doing with his hind feet.

Babe's feet were so big that every time he was shod, Paul had to open a new iron mine. Each of Babe's shoes was so heavy that the blacksmith carrying it sank two feet deep in solid rock with each step he took.

Babe was as strong as he was big. When he tugged at a logging chain of iron links, he soon pulled it out into a solid bar. So the smith was kept busy making new chains.

Babe was blue—a fine, pretty, deep blue— and that is why he was called the blue ox. When a person looked up at him, even the air looked blue around him. Babe's nose was pretty nearly all black, but the nostrils were red, and he had big white horns, curly on the upper section and darkish brown at the tip. The rest of him was all deep blue.

Babe had not always been blue. When he was a little calf, he was white. But he turned blue standing out in the field for six days the first winter of the Blue Snow, and he never got white again. Winter and summer the ox was the same color except probably in July—around the Fourth. Then Babe might perhaps have been just a shade lighter.

Some loggers say that Paul brought Babe from Canada when he was only a few days old—carried him across the border in a sack. And then there are others who say he was a pretty fair-sized calf when Paul got him. According to them, a man near Detroit was supposed to have had Babe first. This man didn't have more than about forty acres on his farm cleared and under cultivation. And naturally that wasn't enough to raise feed for Babe. So the man sold him the year of the Short Oats to Paul Bunyan.

Babe was so strong that he could haul a whole section of timber at a time. He would walk right off with it—the entire six hundred and forty acres—haul it down to the river, and dump it into the water.

Babe had one job in Wisconsin that almost stumped him. That was when he pulled the crooks out of a road. Generally, Babe could walk off with any job, but those crooks were almost more than even he could handle.

Of all the crooked roads in the world, that road was the crookedest. In eighteen miles it doubled back on itself sixteen times. The road made four figure 8's, nine 3's, and four S's. Besides that, it made one each of nearly every other letter in the alphabet.

The trouble with the road was that there was too much of it, and it did not know what to do with itself. So it got into mischief. A man walking along it, unsuspecting, suddenly would see a coil of it lying behind a tree and looking positively ready to spring at him.

While driving over the road, the teamsters met themselves coming back so many times that they nearly went crazy. Paul made up his mind that the road should be straightened.

He brought Babe out right away and hitched him to the near end of the road. Then Paul went up and spoke low to the ox. Babe took hold and came near breaking himself in two.

"Co-ome on, Ba-abe!" coaxed Paul, and Babe pulled as no ox will ever pull again. His hind legs lay straight out behind, and his body stretched out so that it nearly touched the ground. That pull was one of the greatest things Babe ever did—it took out every last crook in the road.

Caring for the ox was no trifling matter. The way he ate, it kept two men busy picking the baling wire out of his teeth at mealtime. Four tons of grain were nothing for Babe to eat at a meal. As for hay, Paul had to move the camp every two weeks to get away from the haywire that collected where Babe ate.

Afterwards, when Paul got a hay farm in Wisconsin, things were easier. The men just raked the hay up in rows and let it freeze out in the fields. In the winter they would haul one end of a row into the stable and cut it up in chunks for Babe, pulling it up a little each time. In that way they did not have the nuisance of haywire. Paul could never keep Babe more than a day or so in any of his smaller camps because it took the teamsters a whole year to haul one day's feed for him.

Sometimes when Babe was in an especially playful mood, he'd lie down in a river so that the water would rise and leave a boom of logs high and dry. Or he would step on a ridge around a lake and smash it down. The water would overflow, flood the river, and drown out all the surrounding countryside.

In camp the men sometimes used to feed Babe flapjacks, and he got awfully fond of them. They were made on a big griddle and folded up in quarters, with clover hay inside. This was a sandwich that Babe really liked.

Paul Bunyan was certainly very fond of his gigantic ox, and very proud of him, too, as he had a right to be!

"Be faithful, Babe," he used to say under his breath, as he walked along beside the ox. "Yes, be faithful, my Babe, faithful."

Later on, Paul heard of an outfit that was logging on the West Coast on a big scale. This outfit was headed by a one-eyed logger named Joe. Paul naturally wanted to go and show that fellow how to log. And he did.

Joe had a pet ostrich, and he challenged Paul to a race between the bird and Babe. Paul wasn't eager to race, but he had to do it to save Babe's reputation.

The Fourth of July was picked for the race, and the track was laid from a point in eastern Canada to one in the western part of the State of Washington.

Paul Bunyan's men were all loyal to Babe. They knew he would win—not because he was so swift, but he was so big that when going slow, or standing still, Babe covered a lot of ground. No ostrich would ever beat him.

Paul had his ox's horns tipped with shiny brass for the occasion, and a flag fluttered from a pole tied onto Babe's tail. Nobody had ever seen him so gay. But the extra weight of the brass and the flag must have bothered Babe. He didn't move a step when the starter signaled. The ostrich was eight miles off before Babe lifted a foot.

But when he did, that was it. In no time the bird was miles behind. Babe arrived in the State of Washington, amid much cheering, six hours before his shadow.

Pecos Bill and the Cyclone

When Pecos Bill was about four years old,
he and his parents and seventeen sisters and
brothers traveled westward through Texas.
Their covered wagon was rattling down to the
Pecos River. Not far from the ford, the rear
left wheel bounced over a great rock. Bill,
his red hair bristling like porcupine quills,
rolled out of the rear of the wagon and landed
in a sand pile. He lay there dazed until the
wagon had crossed the river and disappeared.

He was found a few hours later by Grandy,
a wise coyote who was the undisputed leader
of the coyote packs of Pecos Valley.

Grandy called the boy Crop Ear because his ears weren't like a coyote's. Grandy took the boy home and taught him all about the out-of-doors. He led Crop Ear to berries and nuts and showed the small boy how to find roots that were good to eat.

The coyotes in the pack took a real liking to Crop Ear. They showed him where the field mouse nested, where the song thrush hid her eggs, where the squirrel stored nuts, and where the mountain sheep concealed her young, high among the towering rocks.

Crop Ear became a creature of the plains, not knowing that he was really a human being. He was sturdy and strong and as swift as a bird in flight. By the time he was a young man, he could run with the fleetest coyotes. At night he would squat on his haunches and bark and yip and howl sadly, according to the approved custom of the pack.

The fame of Crop Ear spread widely, for the coyotes bragged about him to everyone they met. To the other animals' knowledge, Crop Ear was the first child to be made into a coyote. And they envied Grandy's pack.

One day Crop Ear had a strange adventure. He was lying among some bushes, resting on his elbows with his chin in his hands, when he heard the dull t-lot, t-lot of an approaching horse. This was not strange. He had often met ponies. But now he was conscious of an odor that puzzled him, for he prided himself on knowing the scents of the various animals in his part of the world.

This smell was so very queer that he sat up and peeked timidly out from the thicket to see what the strange smell might be. There, only a few yards distant, he saw a buckskin-colored pony and its rider come to a halt.

Crop Ear let out three scared yelps. At once Chuck, the pony's rider, who was able to mimic animal sounds, repeated the yelps. This further aroused Crop Ear's curiosity. In coyote language Crop Ear was asking, "Who are you?" and Chuck was repeating this question, not knowing at all what it meant.

Thus began the most amusing conversation in all the history of talk. Crop Ear would bark a question over and over, and in reply Chuck would mimic him perfectly.

Then Chuck, speaking in a subdued voice, started teaching Crop Ear to say words in human language. Slowly at first, Crop Ear began to talk. He was taking up his speech where he had left off years before.

Chuck was amazed at how fast Crop Ear learned. "Who are you?" he kept asking, but Crop Ear recalled only that he was a coyote.

"Who are you?" Crop Ear asked in return.

"My name's Bob Hunt, but the cowboys call me Chuck Wagon because I'm always hungry —Chuck for short. But why do you live here like a coyote? That's what I'd like to know."

"I *am* a coyote," Crop Ear answered.

Chuck cried, "You're not! You're human."

Crop Ear shouted, "I'm not human. Don't

I hunt with the coyote pack and run the legs off the jack rabbits and the antelope? Don't I sit on my haunches and howl every night according to the ancient and approved custom of coyotes? Don't you suppose I know who I am as well as you know who you are? You can't prove that I'm not a noble coyote."

"Come on. I'll give you proof," said Chuck.

He put his foot in the stirrup and spurred his pony toward the Pecos River, with Crop Ear trotting beside him. When they got to the water, Chuck dismounted and found a pool that made a perfect mirror.

"Look at yourself!" Chuck commanded.

In the water Crop Ear saw a creature that looked like Chuck! The thought that he might be human was terrible to Crop Ear. For a long time he stood stunned and motionless. Then he looked at his reflection again.

Just then Chuck caught sight of a mark on Crop Ear's tanned right arm—a tattooed star.

"I'll be locoed if I haven't a tattooed star exactly like that," he cried. "You're my lost brother Bill. You aren't Crop Ear. And you never were."

Chuck continued, "Our mother had a star tattooed on the arm of each of her children so that if one ever got lost, this star would help find him. As usual, Mother was right. You got lost, but you are found again. See?"

Then Chuck told Crop Ear all about his being lost from the wagon at the age of four and not being missed for a whole day because there were eighteen children in the family.

"But when my mother finally discovered I was gone, what then?" Crop Ear asked.

"Well, Mother still had seventeen of us to look after, but she often spoke of little lost Bill. And she never got over missing you."

"Your story sounds reasonable," Crop Ear said at last. "And we do look alike. But I don't want to be *human*."

Chuck was quick to reply. "It's high time you forgot you were ever called Crop Ear. It's right and proper for you to become Pecos Bill! Come back with me to the ranch."

Pecos Bill went to the I X L ranch. It didn't take him long to become boss of the ranch crew, for he was good at managing everything—everything except the weather.

When summer came, the baking sun was unbearable. It scorched the wide prairie for weeks. Streams dried up. Grass withered to a dry yellow. The cattle lolled out their tongues and grew cross.

Then one afternoon there wasn't even the faintest breeze. The heat grew oppressive. A severe, awful silence fell over everything. The cattle stood and drowsed lifelessly.

After a time the herd suddenly changed its mood and became touchy and nervous. The cattle sniffed the air, snorted, and bellowed until they threatened to stampede.

Meanwhile, the sky was becoming more and more inky. "We're in for a tornado!" shouted Pecos, leaping astride his pony. In an instant he was among the cattle. The other riders quickly joined him, and together they got the cattle moving slowly along.

Soon there was a dull roar, and a black funnel moved menacingly from the depths of the greenish-copper darkness. The men noted the direction in which the funnel was moving and turned the cattle to the right of where its central swirl would come.

Between crashes of thunder the men heard a wild "E-yow!" and saw Pecos riding out to meet the cyclone. Clenched in his teeth was a bowie knife. As he neared the funnel, he unfurled his lasso, whirled its loop, and hurled it in defiance at the oncoming monster.

"Pecos Bill's roping the cyclone!" shouted a cowboy. Just then Pecos vaulted into the air and disappeared amid the blackness.

With a whizz, a deafening roar, and a bang, the cyclone leaped directly over the heads of the cowboys and was gone. The men rode along the path of the storm to see whether they could find Pecos. They felt sure he'd been thrown before he could get on top of the funnel. But not a trace of him did they find.

Meantime, Pecos Bill was having the time of his life, whirling about above the clouds.

Across Texas the cyclone tore, bucking and twisting worse than a herd of wild horses. When the crafty cyclone realized it couldn't free itself of Pecos Bill by shaking him off its back, it tried to scare him to death. Reaching down, it pulled up half a dozen mountains by the roots and threw them at Pecos Bill's head.

But Pecos dodged those mountains so fast that the monster cyclone could not see where he was half the time.

When the cyclone saw that mountains were too large and clumsy to handle, it was madder than ever and went racing down across New Mexico. In fact, the cyclone was so perfectly furious that it tore up every tree in its path and cracked it to splinters. The splintered trees were a lot more dangerous than a few loose mountains. Before long, Pecos Bill's whole body was severely bruised, and his clothes were torn to fluttering shreds.

All this, of course, made Pecos unhappy. But he just hung on to the cyclone and never said a single word. And pretty soon the wily old cyclone began to get an idea. It would turn itself into rain and slide right out from under him.

As soon as Pecos Bill realized what was happening, he said to himself, "This cyclone is acting just the way a horse acts when he decides to turn over on his back. I guess the only thing that's left for me to do now is to jump!"

And jump he did—down toward the earth.

Rain was falling in torrents. The water rushed through the great gully the cyclone had cut out between the mountains and, quick as a wink, the water made the Grand Canyon of the Colorado.

Looking at the horizon in every direction, Pecos Bill saw in the Southwest what looked to be a wide cushion of sand. Quickly setting his foot on the top of a mountain over which he was passing, he kicked himself off into space with a gigantic bound.

For what seemed an incredible time, he flew through the air. He was so high that for a while he was afraid he might be flying off the earth. He looked around to see whether the moon was in his immediate vicinity.

Then gradually he saw beneath him what looked like a sea of golden haze reaching up to catch him. Slowly the haze cleared away, and the golden glow became dazzling. Soon it was leaping wildly up toward him, and the next instant there was a terrible crash.

When Pecos Bill came to his senses, he was in the bottom of what seemed to be an enormous shallow bowl. In every direction he could see nothing but an expanse of sand.

The fact was that in falling, he'd splashed out the greatest depression in the Southwest. Down at the bottom he had left the impression of his hip pockets in bedrock. In short, he'd made Death Valley, which is there to this day.

Pecos Bill slowly got to his feet. His body was as sore as a boil, and he couldn't even gather the courage to touch himself to see whether his bones were still inside him. He felt better when he found out he could walk.

Then he remembered something else and opened his left hand, in which he had been carrying a twenty-dollar gold piece. At first he could not believe his eyes. The cyclone had blown his gold piece into two half dollars and a nickel! He took the bowie knife from between his teeth. Here was another jolt! The wind had blown the bowie knife into a dainty pearl-handled penknife.

"I seem to be in the middle of nowhere," Pecos sighed. "What can I do with so little money and such a useless knife?"

Then a smile spread over his face. He couldn't be beaten by trifles after he'd busted a cyclone. He sniffed the air and galloped off, coyote fashion, toward the I X L ranch.

The King's Stilts

Naturally the king *never* wore his stilts during business hours. When King Birtram worked, he really WORKED, and his stilts stood forgotten in the tall stilt closet in the castle's front hallway.

There was so much work to be done in the kingdom of Binn that King Birtram had to get up every morning at five. Long before the townsfolk and the farmers were awake, the king was splashing away in his bath. It was right there, in fact, that his day's work began. With his left hand he could bathe with his royal bath brush, but his right hand he always had to keep dry for signing the important papers of state.

Eric, his page boy, brought in these papers on a big silver tray. He stood at attention at the foot of the tub, while old Lord Droon took the papers, one by one, and held them over the water for His Majesty to sign.

"Sign here . . . sign there," old Droon would say. "And hurry, Sire, hurry. There are hundreds more to come."

It was just the same at breakfast. The king cut and buttered his toast with only his left hand. With his right he kept signing royal orders and commands.

By seven every morning the king had always finished more business than most kings do in a month. He *had* to get all this done before seven, for that was the hour when his big work commenced—the most difficult and important work in the whole kingdom of Binn.

This was the work of caring for the mighty dike trees that protected the people of Binn from the sea. The sea pushed against the kingdom on three sides. The kingdom was a low one; the sea was a high one; and only the dike trees kept the sea from pouring in. They grew so close together in a row along the shore that they held back the water with their heavy, knotted roots.

But to keep these trees strong and sturdy was not an easy task. They were more spicy than pine trees, and their roots were very tasty to a certain sort of bird. This was a kind of giant blackbird with a sharp and pointed beak. Nizzards they were called by the people of Binn. These nizzards were always flying about over the dike trees, waiting for a chance to swoop down and peck. If nobody stopped them, the roots would soon give way. Then the sea would pour in with a terrible roar, and every last soul in the kingdom would drown. But King Birtram did not permit this to happen.

He had gathered together in his kingdom the largest and the smartest cats in all the world, and had trained them to chase the nizzards away. These cats were called patrol cats and wore badges that said "P. C."

"Everything in Binn," said King Birtram, "depends on our patrol cats. They are more important than our army, our navy, and our fire department, too, for they keep the nizzards away from the dike trees, and the dike trees keep the ocean back out of our land."

A thousand cats in all! They divided up the work. Five hundred guarded the kingdom by day; the other five hundred kept watch through the night.

At seven every morning came the changing of the cat guard. At the sound of a trumpet the king left his breakfast and mounted his horse for the daily review. Fresh, brisk, and well fed, the five hundred day cats marched past him toward the dike trees to take up their watch. At the same time the night cats, muddy, tired, and hungry, headed home to their kennels for their twelve hours' rest.

There was rest for the cats. There was none for the king. It took every minute of his morning to see that they were given the very best of care. The huts that they slept in must be kept clean and tidy. Each cat must be brushed, and his whiskers trimmed just so. The cat kitchen was even bigger and grander than the king's. And the cooks who did the cooking were the chief cooks in the land.

"Your Majesty," the chief-in-charge-of-fish would always say, "tell us that you think the food we feed our cats is perfect." And the king would look over the huge wet baskets of fish, choosing only the finest and the freshest to serve to his patrol cats.

So went the morning. Then all afternoon, both in winter and summer, the king made his rounds by the edge of the sea. Every root of every dike tree he inspected every day.

But finally, at five o'clock, the great task was finished!

Then the king smiled. "A hard day," he'd say, "full of nizzardly worries. A long day," he'd say. *"Now it's time for some fun!"*

This was the moment King Birtram lived for. When he worked, he really worked . . . but when he played, he really PLAYED!

"Quick, Eric!" he'd shout. "Quick, Eric! The stilts!"

Down the slope from the dike trees, away from all troubles, the king and Eric would race like two boys—straight to the tall stilt closet in the castle's front hallway.

Out came the stilts! Up leaped the king!

High in the air, his royal robes streaming, he'd race through the marble halls . . . out across the terrace . . . up and down the garden stairs. Black-spotted coach dogs barked and romped beside him, nipping at the heels of his flashing red stilts.

The townsfolk looked on from the walls and just loved it. "A grown-up king on stilts," they'd say, *"does* look rather strange. But it's hard work being king, and he does his work well. If he wants to have a bit of fun . . . sure! . . . let him have it!"

But there was one man in Binn who didn't like fun. He didn't like games. He didn't like laughing. This man was a scowler. This man was Lord Droon. "Laughing spoils the shape of the face," he declared. "The lines at the corners of the mouth should go *down*."

Every afternoon when the stilt hour drew near, Lord Droon would slink away to his room in the northwest tower and sulk. *"Such carryings on!"* he would mutter in disgust, as he spied on the king from his window. *"Look at his crown!* Bouncing up and down on the side of his head! *Look at his beard!* Flapping in the wind! *Look at him laughing!* Right out in broad daylight in front of the townsfolk! . . . I must do something about this."

And one day he did. One Wednesday just before supper, when he thought the king was out, Lord Droon tiptoed down to the front hall. The guards at their posts were dozing. Without the smallest sound on the hard stone floor, Droon crept to the stilt closet, pulled back the ancient door, and reached in. . . .

It took only a second. He had the king's stilts! He unbuttoned the top of his long robe and shoved them inside. Then he sneaked past the guards again and slipped through the door. Down the steep, slanting stairway Lord Droon marched with the stilts. Down to the furnace to burn them! "This is the end of the king's foolish stilt-walking," he mumbled.

Then suddenly, from around the bend of the stairs below, came the sound of happy whistling. The king!

Lord Droon stopped still, almost frozen with fright. He tugged and pulled at his long flowing gown, struggling to cover the stilts. But he couldn't. The ends were too long and stuck out. "Droon! Droon!" gasped Lord Droon. "You'll be caught!" He turned and fled back up the stairway.

Nearer and nearer came the king, but Droon couldn't climb any faster. The stilts clattered; they banged and spanked against his knees.

He looked up and saw a window. Stepping up to it quickly, he poked his head out. He looked down into an alley. A small boy was passing. It was Eric, the page boy.

"Psst . . . you . . . *you* . . ." Lord Droon hissed in a hoarse, nervous whisper.

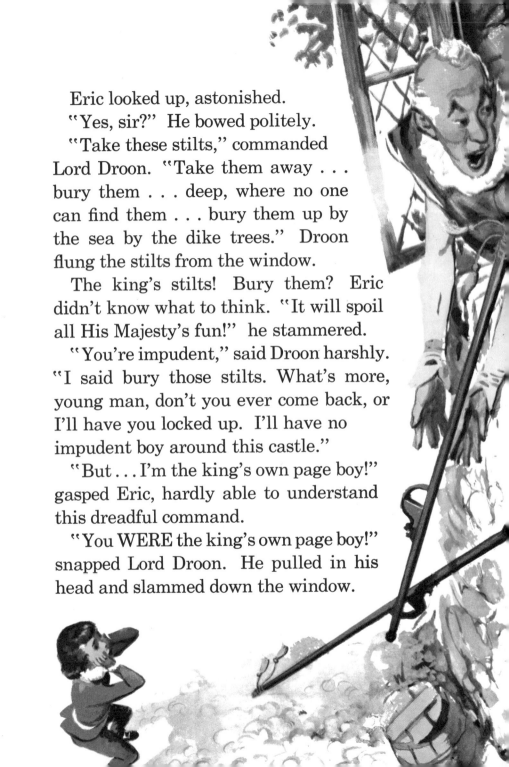

Eric looked up, astonished.

"Yes, sir?" He bowed politely.

"Take these stilts," commanded Lord Droon. "Take them away . . . bury them . . . deep, where no one can find them . . . bury them up by the sea by the dike trees." Droon flung the stilts from the window.

The king's stilts! Bury them? Eric didn't know what to think. "It will spoil all His Majesty's fun!" he stammered.

"You're impudent," said Droon harshly. "I said bury those stilts. What's more, young man, don't you ever come back, or I'll have you locked up. I'll have no impudent boy around this castle."

"But . . . I'm the king's own page boy!" gasped Eric, hardly able to understand this dreadful command.

"You WERE the king's own page boy!" snapped Lord Droon. He pulled in his head and slammed down the window.

Never before had Eric been so puzzled. Never in his life had he felt so sad. But there was nothing to do but obey the command. He picked up the stilts and walked straight toward the road that led to the sea.

It was the hour that the townsfolk were all having supper. Nobody saw him dig the deep hole. Nobody saw him bury the stilts.

At five the next afternoon the halls of the castle echoed the king's mournful shouts. "Droon . . . ! They're gone! *They're gone!*" The king stood groping in the stilt closet, hopelessly searching for what wasn't there.

Lord Droon chuckled to himself. He had expected this to happen and was ready with his lie. "It was the townsfolk who did it," he said, peering into the stilt closet and pretending to be greatly shocked. "I have seen them every day, plotting behind the castle walls. 'A king,' they say, 'should behave like a king, and sit with pomp and dignity upon his royal throne. A king,' they say, 'should never walk on stilts!' It's too bad, Your Majesty, but you must try to do without them."

King Birtram answered with a heartbroken sigh. "Well . . . I'll *try* to do without them."

But he couldn't.

Day after day he grew sadder and sadder. For long hours he'd just sit, idly drumming with his fingers on the arms of his throne.

He couldn't keep his mind on his work. His commands to the patrol cats sounded feeble and faint. The cats seemed to know it and wouldn't obey.

Day by day they grew lazier and lazier.

Uncombed and unbrushed, they slept most of the day and grew fat. No one bothered to put their P.C. badges on them, for as chasers of nizzards they weren't worth a thing.

Day by day the nizzards grew bolder and bolder. They cackled and fluttered over the dike trees. They flew down and almost seemed to sneer at the lazy, sleeping cats.

The townsfolk began to feel frightened. Housewives couldn't keep their minds on

their housework. They heard nizzards flapping over their roof tops and poked their heads out for a look. "If the cats don't keep those nizzards away from our dike trees," they asked one another, "what will keep the ocean back out of our land?"

Bootmakers couldn't keep their minds on their boots. Goldsmiths couldn't keep their minds on their gold. Cart drivers couldn't keep their minds on where they were going. They'd stop their carts on the road and talk in low, excited whispers. "Look at those nizzards. . . ! Where *are* the cats?"

"I'll tell you where they are . . . everywhere they shouldn't be and mostly fast asleep."

"Something must be wrong with the king."

"Yes, something's certainly wrong with the king!"

Only Eric, the page boy, knew what was wrong. Night after night he tossed in his bed, thinking of the stilts deep underground. Finally, one night he could stand it no longer. Droon or no Droon, he would go to the king!

At dawn the next day he leaped out of bed and made straight for the castle.

Breathless and panting, he raced through the royal gates and up the broad stairs.

The king was strolling sadly on the terrace, with Lord Droon and two guards.

Eric rushed up. He *must* tell the king. Droon or no Droon, he was going to tell.

But Lord Droon saw him coming and stepped quickly forward. "Impudent boy, what are *you* doing here?"

Before Eric could answer and push past him to the king, Lord Droon had grabbed him. He looked at Eric sharply, and suddenly the corners of his mouth turned up in a grin. A shrewd, evil grin. "Your face . . . !" he said. *"What's wrong with your face?"*

"My face . . . ?" said Eric. He rubbed his hand over his forehead. It was merely hot and moist from running. "Nothing at all is wrong with my face."

"It's red," said Lord Droon, with the sly look he always had when he lied. "It's awfully, awfully RED. MEASLES!" he shouted. "Ho, guards . . . take him away! Lock him up!"

"I haven't measles any more than you have," shouted Eric. "It's a trick—a nasty, Droonish trick! Let me talk to the king."

But they dragged poor Eric, fighting and kicking, away from the king and down the castle stairs. Five minutes later Eric found himself locked up in an old deserted house on the edge of the town.

From his second-story window he could see the two guards, spears crossed, just below him, barring the door. Through the roof he could hear the noises of the nizzards. Their beaks were hard as iron and scratched through the air.

Eric shuddered. There *must* be a way to escape. Round and round the room he paced, thinking and thinking.

He went to the window and looked down again. Then he whistled softly. He had an idea.

Very quickly Eric slipped off his belt. He pushed the end through the buckle and made a lasso. Then he leaned from the window and aimed for the spear points. He dropped the loop. It caught! He jerked the belt tight and tied a quick knot. "Look, guards, look!" shouted Eric, as he jumped up on the window sill. "Your spears are tied together!"

If the guards had dropped their spears, they could have caught him in a second. But they didn't. They just yelled at each other, and yanked and tugged, stupidly trying to pull the spears apart. By the time they finally had them untied, Eric had sprung to the tree outside his window, slid down the trunk, and quietly escaped.

Eric ran.

Through back yards and alleyways to escape the angry guards! The streets were deserted. No people at all! They were all at home, trembling, with their window shades pulled down.

The air was full of the chittering and the chattering of nizzards. They were cutting through the clouds like flying black knives ... flying nearer ... flying lower ... down to earth to eat the dike tree roots ... soon to let the sea pour in.

Eric ran.

He turned a corner. He stopped and stared with horror! Flowing gently toward him down the sloping alley came a little trickling stream. "Water!" he whispered hoarsely. He dipped in his finger. It tasted of salt. *"Sea* water!" One dike tree must already have been eaten clean through!

"Not a second to lose," gasped Eric. "I must dig up the stilts."

Up the hill to the dike trees where the king's stilts lay buried . . . right into the very thick of the nizzards! They flapped and screeched about him. They hissed as he dug.

"G-r-ritch . . . !" snarled the nizzards.

"*G-r-ritch* to *you!*" snapped back Eric, furiously pelting them with fistfuls of mud.

The harder they fought him, the faster he dug. His fingers touched the stilts at last. He pulled them from the ground.

Stilts bouncing on his shoulder, again Eric ran. The road to the castle took him back through town. The streets were still deserted.

Close by the door of an old tailor shop Eric stopped for an instant to rest. The stilts had begun to hurt his shoulder. "Those two stupid guards," he thought. "I wonder where *they* are." He found out all too soon.

From around the corner, at his very elbow, suddenly bellowed the angry voice of old Lord Droon. "You *guards!* Guards, indeed! To let a little pipsqueak of a boy tie up your spears. *Dunderheads!* Search every street . . . search every house. . . ." Eric heard the clatter of their heavy hobnail boots. No time to run.

Nowhere to hide. Wait . . . ! Those clothes in the tailor shop . . . ! Eric ducked inside.

An instant later Lord Droon and the guards appeared around the corner. "Search that tailor shop first!" commanded Lord Droon.

But just as he said this, from out of the shop strode a strange, tall man. There was something very odd about the hang of his robe. His hat was pulled down far over his eyes.

"Those eyes. . . ." muttered Droon. "Have I seen them before?" He stepped in front of the tall man, blocking his path.

The tall man's mouth went suddenly dry.

"Are you . . . are you . . ." he stammered hoarsely, "are you by any chance seeking a small boy with no belt?"

"Which way?" shouted the guards. "Which way did he go?"

"That way," said Eric, and he nodded toward the sea.

With a clatter of hobnails the two guards were off, Lord Droon sputtering and scolding along behind them.

"No time to shrink down to a boy again," thought Eric. "I'll have to stay a tall man."

On to the castle Eric raced in his disguise, over fences and thickets, through orchards and fields of corn. Everywhere he saw patrol cats, useless and limp, fast asleep on haystacks, dozing in the trees.

Then suddenly, just ahead, he saw the king. He was sitting on a little pile of stones just outside the castle gate. His robe wasn't pressed; his crown wasn't shined; and he had deep, sad circles under both of his eyes.

"Your Majesty . . . Your Majesty!" shouted Eric as he clattered up behind him.

The king paid no attention. Eric leaned down and shouted right into his ear. Very slowly the king turned his head.

"Well," sighed King Birtram, "and who may *you* be?"

"I'm Eric!" cried Eric. He let the robe that was covering him drop to the ground. The king's own red stilts flashed bright in the sun.

Down from the stilts leaped Eric, the page boy. Up onto the stilts sprang Birtram, the king. He drew a great kingly breath—the first one in weeks. His head shot up high; his chest broadened wide.

Birtram of Binn
was sturdy, straight,
and strong again, and
every inch a king.

"PATROL CATS!"

It was the loudest
command ever shouted
in Binn. The king's voice
seemed to roll up from deep
in his boots. It echoed down the
valleys; it rumbled through the hills.

From wherever they had wandered, the cats heard the call. They fell in line; they fell in step; they marched ahead a thousand strong. Up the hill to the dike trees they followed Eric and the king.

"Day cats to the left flank . . . ! Night cats to the right! *Charge!*" the king shouted.

A hundred thousand nizzards stopped their pecking and sprang to meet the charge. The dike trees shook as the cats roared their war cry. The sea's surface swirled into wild, raging whirlpools. The noise was heard five hundred miles away. The fur flew fast, but the feathers flew faster!

It took only ten minutes. The kingdom was saved! The townsfolk stopped trembling indoors behind their window shades. They rushed out from their houses and filled the air with cheers.

Then the king punished Droon in a most fitting way. He sent him to live by himself with a guard of patrol cats in that old deserted house with the sign that said MEASLES. And he made him eat nizzards three times every day. Stewed nizzards for breakfast. Cold nizzards for lunch. Fried nizzards for supper. And . . . every other Thursday they served him nizzard hash.

But to Eric, his page boy, the king gave a fine and just reward. He ordered the royal carpenter to make another pair of stilts . . . tall stilts, red and flashing, exactly like his own. From then on, every day at five they always raced on stilts together. And when they played, they really PLAYED. And when they worked, they really WORKED. And the cats kept the nizzards away from the dike trees. And the dike trees kept the water back out of the land.

BOOKS TO READ

Here are some good books that provide more of the same fun and adventure we find in the new *Days and Deeds*.

Young Citizens of Today

Eddie and Gardenia.   Carolyn Haywood.
Eddie and his mischievous goat, Gardenia, find a new world of fun and adventure on Uncle Ed's ranch in Texas. You will want to find out how Eddie gets to be a real cowboy and what he does when Gardenia gets caught in a catclaw bush.

Katie John.   Mary Calhoun.
Katie John Tucker moves with her family into an old house inherited from Aunt Emily. At first Katie doesn't like the old house. However, being a girl that acts before she thinks, Katie discovers many secrets about the house that change her mind.

Little Leaguer's First Uniform.   C. Paul Jackson.
When Johnny's brother, Hank, gets the mumps, Johnny plays in his place in a Little League World Series. Johnny is afraid that he will disgrace Hank's uniform, but you will be surprised how he manages to help his team.

Pete's Home Run.   Marion Renick.
Pete hopes to play baseball on his older brother's Little League team someday. He is looking for the easy way, until he finally learns through practice to keep his eye on the ball and to swing his bat. You will also like *Nicky's Football Team*, another book by this author.

Rowena Carey.   Ruth Langland Holberg.
Rowena wants a horse more than anything else in the world. Row's ideas of how to earn money to buy a horse lead to many funny experiences in the seacoast village where she lives. Be sure to read *Tomboy Row* by the same author, too.

Sandy's Spurs.   Lavinia R. Davis.

When Sandy goes to Virginia for a vacation, he plans to spend his time bird-spotting. First he finds himself a P.G. (paying guest). Next Sandy is thrown from a horse. Then he joins forces with three friends to solve the mystery of a family treasure.

Silver Spurs for Cowboy Boots.   Shannon Garst.

Bob spends a second summer on his uncle's cattle ranch in Wyoming. A mystery man, a wild-horse roundup, a stampede, and a rodeo add to the excitement of Bob's summer. If you have not read *Cowboy Boots*, the story of Bob's first summer on the ranch, you will enjoy reading it, too.

Thimble Summer.   Elizabeth Enright.

Garnet finds a silver thimble, which she is sure will bring her luck, and it does. The long spell of dry weather ends, and Garnet's adventures begin. A strange boy, a secret journey, and a day at the fair all help make Garnet's "thimble summer" wonderful and exciting.

Windy Foot at the County Fair.   Frances Frost.

In four exciting days at the County Fair, Toby and his pony, Windy Foot, make new friends. You will especially want to find out what happens when he and Windy Foot enter the pony race. Other books about this pony are *Sleigh Bells for Windy Foot* and *Maple Sugar for Windy Foot*, both good stories of life on a New England farm.

Moving Westward

Bronco Charlie: Rider of the Pony Express.   Henry V. Larom.

Charlie is almost twelve and wants to be a Pony Express rider. One day he gets a chance to carry the mail when a horse comes in without a rider. This short book tells about his exciting trip and what happens afterwards that makes Charlie very proud and happy.

Caddie Woodlawn.   Carol Ryrie Brink.
Caddie is the despair of her mother and sister because she is
such a tomboy, but she is well fitted for pioneer life on a
Wisconsin farm during the 1860's. She makes friends with
Indian John and has some exciting adventures when people
hear that the Indians are on the warpath.

Children of the Covered Wagon.   Mary Jane Carr.
Jim, Jerry, and Myra are three children who travel in a wagon
train that sets out from Independence, Missouri, for Oregon
in 1844. Each part of their dangerous two-thousand-mile
journey is vividly described—the fording of rivers, Indian
attacks, life at the forts, and the long struggle over the
mountains.

His Indian Brother.   Hazel Wilson.
Because of unexpected circumstances, Brad Porter is left
alone in a pioneer cabin in the Maine wilderness. Brad would
have starved to death without the help of Sabattis, an Indian
boy. Sabattis teaches Brad to trap, fish, and hunt. The courage of the two boys until the return of Brad's father makes
an exciting story.

Johnny Texas.   Carol Hoff.
When Johann comes to America in 1834, the Texas stage-
coach driver tells him that he is "Johnny" in Texas. So
Johnny Texas he becomes. In spite of storms and floods and
trouble with Mexico, Johnny loves his life in the new world.
The surprise at the end is worth waiting for.

North to Abilene.   Zachary Ball.
Seth Hartley, a thirteen-year-old boy, has no home or parents
—nothing of his own but a big, black bull. Both Seth and the
bull are befriended by Amos Keedy, a cattleman. Seth learns
to shoot, rope, ride, and tend cattle. The great demand
for meat in the northern part of the country prompts an
adventure-filled cattle drive from Texas to Abilene, Kansas.

On the Banks of Plum Creek. Laura Ingalls Wilder.
Laura and her family live in a dugout on the banks of Plum Creek in Minnesota. She and her sister Mary play on the riverbanks and have many adventures. There is a runaway, as well as a flood, a prairie fire, and a blizzard. You will also enjoy *By the Shores of Silver Lake,* another book about this pioneer family by the same author.

The California Gold Rush. May McNeer.
This is a thrilling account of the days when men poured into California from all over the world in a feverish search for gold. This book is one of the famous Landmark series, and each chapter is a story in itself.

The Pony Express. Samuel Hopkins Adams.
Day after day for nineteen months, the Pony Express managed to do the impossible. Here is the story of the brave riders who carried the mail across the country in spite of accidents, violent storms, and attacks by Indians. This exciting book is another in the Landmark series.

Treasure in the Covered Wagon. Vera Graham.
The story in your book contains only a few of the exciting events that happened on Flave-Ann's trip to Oregon with her reed organ. More than once she thought the organ was gone for good. The author says that the story is a true one.

Tree in the Trail. Holling Clancy Holling.
For more than two hundred years, from 1610 to 1834, a great cottonwood tree grew beside an Indian trail that later became the famous Santa Fe Trail. The tree's story is a tale of Indians, explorers, and pioneer settlers in the great Southwest.

Tree Wagon. Evelyn Sibley Lampman.
When the Luelling family travels to Oregon, they take a wagon loaded with seven hundred young trees to plant in the new country. Slowly, young Seenie learns to love the trees. The story tells of the family's long trip and of how the tree wagon saves the family from Indian attacks.

Wonders of Today

A Race for Bill.   May Nickerson Wallace.
Bill Mason is really afraid to enter the Soapbox Derby, but when everyone urges him to fix up his old Meatball, he does. In spite of an accident to his racer and a broken left arm, he finishes his car in time to enter the race. What happens then makes an exciting story.

Codes and Secret Writing.   Herbert S. Zim.
This book is not easy to read, but if you are especially interested in how codes are made and "broken," and if you want to do secret writing, this book will tell you how. It contains practice exercises for simple codes and tells where you can get more detailed information.

Everyday Machines and How They Work.   Herman Schneider.
This book explains the way different pieces of modern household equipment work. The clever black-and-white drawings help make the explanations even more clear. You will learn about all sorts of machines, from egg beaters to vacuum cleaners. You will even learn something about a trumpet!

Experiments with Electricity.   Nelson F. Beeler and Franklyn M. Branley.   This book gives directions for experiments with electricity. The materials you need are listed at the beginning of each chapter and the pictures show you what to do. Some of the experiments like Yehudi's flashlight and a nose that lights up, seem almost magic unless you know the real reason why they work.

Henry Reed, Inc.   Keith Robertson.
Henry Reed and Midge, the girl next door, want to earn money. They think of many unusual ways of doing it. Most of their money-making plans include the use of a wonder of today. Many of their plans are sucecssful, and all of their adventures are funny.

Mr. Bell Invents the Telephone.   Katherine B. Shippen.
This is the interesting story of Alexander Graham Bell, who
starts out to be a teacher of the deaf and ends up inventing
the telephone. He has many difficulties, and people are slow
to accept his invention. This is another Landmark Book.

Television Works Like This.   Jeanne and Robert Bendick.
The many drawings in this book will help you find out how
television works. You will learn about the different jobs that
people do and how the programs that you see in your living
room are made from beginning to end.

The First Book of Airplanes.   Jeanne Bendick.
If you are interested in airplanes and what makes them fly,
you will probably like this short book. It gives clear, accu-
rate information in drawings and in words about many different kinds of planes. You will also learn something about
the history of flight in this book.

The Little Horse That Raced a Train.   Wilma Pitchford Hays.
High in the Colorado mountains, Elmer watches every day
for the horse that races the construction train on which Elmer
rides to school. One day a snowstorm comes, and Elmer sees
the horse trapped on a mountain top. The boy's quick thinking, radio, television, and a helicopter bring aid to the horse.
This thrilling story is based on a true happening.

Three Boys and a Tugboat.   Nan Hayden Agle and Ellen Wilson.
Abercrombie, Benjamin, and Christopher and their dog, John
Paul Jones, make a visit to Uncle Stitch's tugboat, the Kitti-
wake. The boys learn about tugboats and life in a busy port,
but the dog first gets seasick, then he gets lost. When the
boys go hunting for him on Old Fort Island, they find something else, which brings them a reward.

What's Inside of Engines?   Herbert S. Zim.
This little book shows you what goes on inside steam engines,
Diesels, gasoline and jet engines, rockets, and atomic piles.
Even grown-ups like this book.

Storyland of Here and Now

Big Steve: The Double Quick Tunnelman. Marie Halun Bloch.
This tall tale is about Big Steve and his rock hog, Daisy.
Together they dig some mighty tunnels. You will especially
enjoy their funny adventures with the Texas mosquitoes and
with the twenty thousand bats and the part where Daisy gets
"gold fever." The pictures are fun, too.

Charlotte's Web. E. B. White.
Fern persuades her father not to kill the runty pig. She raises
him on a bottle and names him Wilbur, but later she has to
sell him to Uncle Homer. Then she discovers that she can
understand the language of the animals in her uncle's barn.
So she knows that Charlotte, the spider, has a clever plan
to keep Wilbur from being made into bacon. What happens
is very funny and a bit sad.

Horton Hatches the Egg. Dr. Seuss.
If you enjoy "The King's Stilts," you will want to read this
story by the same author about Mayzie, a lazy bird, who persuades Horton, the elephant, to sit on her egg while she takes
a vacation. Faithfully he sits on the egg, through thunder-
storms, winter and spring, while Mayzie lolls in Palm Beach.
The end of it all is very funny. For more of the same kind
of fun, be sure to read this author's *Scrambled Eggs Super*
and *McElligot's Pool.*

Just So Stories. Rudyard Kipling.
When you have read "How the Camel Got His Hump," you
will be eager to read the rest of this book. Some of the fun-
niest tales tell how the whale got his throat, how the elephant
got his trunk, and how the alphabet was made. The stories
are best when someone reads them aloud.

Mr. Popper's Penguins. Richard and Florence Atwater.
Mr. Popper had never been out of Stillwater, but he was
always dreaming about far-off places. Then suddenly he re-
ceives a penguin from the South Pole. You'll be surprised how

Captain Cook, the penguin, changes the lives of the whole Popper family, and you will laugh at their adventures.

Ol' Paul, the Mighty Logger.   Glen Rounds.
If you like the story "Babe, the Blue Ox," you will certainly want to read this book. It tells more tall tales about Paul and his wonderful Babe. You will chuckle when you read how they got rid of the bedcats and how Paul built the Rocky Mountains.

Pecos Bill: The Greatest Cowboy of All Time.   James C. Bowman.
"Pecos Bill and the Cyclone" in your book relates only one of Bill's amazing feats. Read this book, by the same author, and learn how Bill invented modern cowpunching and why he is the most wonderful cowboy of all time.

The Adventures of Pinocchio.   C. Collodi.
Pinocchio is a mischievous little puppet who starts his tricks as soon as Geppetto finishes carving his hands. The Talking Cricket and the Blue Fairy try to help Pinocchio be good, and he does try, but then he gets into trouble again. What finally becomes of Pinocchio makes a funny and delightful story.

The Fast Sooner Hound.   Arna Bontemps and Jack Conroy.
This short book tells a gay and funny tale about a fast dog that would sooner run than eat. The dog races all sorts of trains, including the speedy Cannon Ball. The pictures are wonderful!

Winnie-the-Pooh.   A. A. Milne.
"Edward Bear, known to his friends as Winnie-the-Pooh, or Pooh for short" is a bear of very little brain. This book tells how he goes visiting and gets stuck, what happens when Eeyore, the donkey, loses his tail, how Piglet meets a heffalump, and other stories. If you like the story about Pooh and Piglet that is in your book, you will like these other stories, too. *The House at Pooh Corner* tells more about the adventures of these friends.

301

GLOSSARY

Full Pronunciation Key

The pronunciation of each word is shown just after the word, in this way: **ab bre vi ate** (ə brē′vi āt). The letters and signs used are pronounced as in the words below. The mark ′ is placed after a syllable with primary or heavy accent, as in the example above. The mark ′ after a syllable shows a secondary or lighter accent, as in **ab bre vi a tion** (ə brē′vi ā′shən).

a	hat, cap	j	jam, enjoy	u	cup, butter
ā	age, face	k	kind, seek	u̇	full, put
ã	care, air	l	land, coal	ü	rule, move
ä	father, far	m	me, am	ū	use, music
		n	no, in		
b	bad, rob	ng	long, bring	v	very, save
ch	child, much			w	will, woman
d	did, red	o	hot, rock	y	young, yet
		ō	open, go		
e	let, best	ô	order, all	z	zero, breeze
ē	equal, be	oi	oil, voice	zh	measure, seizure
ėr	term, learn	ou	house, out		
				ə	represents:
		p	paper, cup		a in about
f	fat, if	r	run, try		e in taken
g	go, bag	s	say, yes		i in pencil
h	he, how	sh	she, rush		o in lemon
		t	tell, it		u in circus
i	it, pin	th	thin, both		
ī	ice, five	ŦH	then, smooth		

This pronunciation key is from the *Thorndike-Barnhart Junior Dictionary*. Special acknowledgment is made to Clarence L. Barnhart, editor of the Thorndike-Barnhart Dictionaries, for his assistance in the preparation of this glossary.

302

a breast (ə brest′), side by side: *The soldiers marched four abreast.*

ab sorb (ab sôrb′), **1.** take in or suck up (liquids): *A blotter absorbs ink.* **2.** take up all the attention of; interest very much: *The boy was absorbed in building a bridge over the brook.*

ac cord (ə kôrd′), **1.** agree; be in harmony: *His account of the day accords with yours.* **2.** agreement; harmony.

according to, **1.** in agreement with: *He came according to his promise.* **2.** on the facts given by (a person, book, etc.): *According to this book a tiger is really a big cat.*

ac count (ə kount′), **1.** statement; story: *The boy gave his father an account of the ball game.* **2.** statement of money received and spent; record of business: *Stores, banks, and factories keep accounts.* **3. On account of** means because of.

ad just (ə just′), arrange; set just right; change to make fit.

a lu mi num (ə lü′mə nəm), a silver-white, very light metal· that does not lose its brightness easily. Aluminum is much used for making kettles and pans.

an cient (ān′shənt), **1.** belonging to times long past: *We saw the ruins of an ancient building constructed six thousand years ago.* **2.** very old: *an ancient city.*

an te lope (an′tə lōp), any one of certain animals somewhat like deer. See the picture.

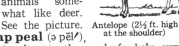
Antelope (2½ ft. high at the shoulder)

ap peal (ə pēl′), **1.** ask earnestly; apply for help, sympathy, etc.: *The children appealed to their mother when they were in* trouble. **2.** an earnest request; a call to the feelings: *Jane made an appeal to her father to forgive her.*

ap prove (ə prüv′), think well of; be pleased with: *The teacher approved Ann's work.*

a rouse (ə rouz′), **1.** awaken. **2.** excite; stir to action.

as sure (ə shür′), tell confidently: *The captain of the ship assured the passengers that there was no danger.*

at tach (ə tach′), **1.** fasten (to): *The boy attached a rope to his sled.* **2.** join.

at tach ment (ə tach′mənt), thing attached. A sewing machine has various attachments, such as a buttonhole maker and a darner.

Au rar i a (ô rār′i ə).

bal ance (bal′əns), **1.** a condition of not falling over in any direction; steadiness: *He lost his balance and fell off the ladder.* **2.** keep or put in a balanced condition.

bass[1] (bās), having a deep, low sound: *a bass voice.*

bass[2] (bas), a fish used for food, living in fresh water or in the ocean.

bathe (bāᵺ), **1.** take a bath. **2.** give a bath to. **3.** go swimming; go into a river, lake, or ocean for sport or to get cool. **4.** pour over; cover: *The valley was bathed in sunlight.*

ben e fit (ben′ə fit), **1.** anything which is for the good of a person or thing. **2.** a program, a game, etc., to raise money which goes to a special person or persons or to a cause.

be wil der (bi wil′dər), confuse completely; puzzle: *She was bewildered by the crowds and noises.*

be wil der ment (bi wil′dər mənt), bewildered condition; confusion.

black smith (blak′smith′), man who works with iron. Blacksmiths can mend tools and shoe horses.

bluff (bluf),   a high, steep bank or cliff.

bow ie knife (bō′i nīf′),   a long hunting knife carried in a case.

cel e bra tion (sel′ə brā′shən),   special program or events given for a certain person, day, or time: *A Fourth of July celebration often includes fireworks.*

chal lenge (chal′ənj),   **1.** question (a person, or something he says, etc.) as if not believing him. **2.** doubt; demand proof of before one will accept. **3.** invitation to a contest, game, or match. **4.** invite to a contest, game, or match.

cham ois (sham′i),   **1.** a small goat-like   antelope. See the picture. **2.** a soft leather made from the skin of sheep, goats, deer, etc.

chant (chant),   **1.** say in a singing voice. **2.** keep talking about; say over and over again.

Chamois (2 ft. high at the shoulder)

chuck wag on (chuk′ wag′ən),   in the Western United States, a wagon that carried food and cooking equipment for cowboys.

clos et (kloz′it),   a small room used for storing clothes or household supplies.

co co nut or **co coa-nut** (kō′kə nut′),   the large, round, brown, hard-shelled fruit of the coco palm. Coconuts have a white lining that is good to eat and a white liquid called coconut milk. The white lining is cut up into shreds and used for cakes and pies.

Coco palm

Col o rad o (kol′ə rad′ō or kol′-ə rä′dō),   **1.** a Western State of the United States. **2.** a river in Southwestern United States.

con fi dent (kon′fə dənt),   fully trusting; certain: *I feel confident that our team will win.*

con scious (kon′shəs),   knowing; having experience; aware: *She was not conscious of the fact that he was in the room.*

con trol (kən trōl′),   **1.** command; have in one's power: *The captain controls his boat.* **2.** hold back: *It is hard to control one's anger.*

cred it (kred′it),   praise; honor.

crew (krü),   group of people working or acting together.

cul ti va tion (kul′tə vā′shən),   **1.** preparing land and growing crops by plowing, planting, and necessary care. **2.** Under cultivation means used for the growing of crops.

cu ri os i ty (kūr′i os′ə ti),   **1.** eager desire to know: *Her curiosity made her open the forbidden door.* **2.** a strange, rare object.

cur rent (kèr′ənt),   **1.** flow of water, air, or any liquid; running stream. **2.** flow of electricity through a wire, etc.

cur ry (kèr′i),   rub and clean (a horse) with a brush or scraper.

cush ion (kùsh′ən),   **1.** a soft pillow for a chair, etc. **2.** anything that makes a soft place: *a cushion of moss.*

deaf (def),   **1.** not able to hear. **2.** not able to hear well.

deaf en (def′ən),   **1.** make deaf. **2.** stun with noise.

de fi ance (di fī′əns),   defying.

de fy (di fī′),   **1.** set oneself openly against (authority): *Now that the boy was earning his own living he could defy his father's harsh rules.* **2.** challenge (a person) to do or prove something.

de lude (di lüd´), mislead; make (a person) believe as true something that is not true.

de pos it (di poz´it), **1.** put down: *He deposited his bundles on the table.* **2.** laying down material by natural means; the material laid down: *deposits of tin.* **3.** put in a place for safekeeping.

de pres sion (di presh´ən), a hollow: *Water filled the depressions in the ground.*

de tail (di tāl´ or dē´tāl), **1.** a small or unimportant part. **2.** dealing with small things one by one: *She does not enjoy the details of housekeeping.*

de ter mi na tion (di tėr´mə nā´shən), fixed purpose; great firmness in carrying out a purpose: *Tom's determination was not weakened by the difficulties he met.*

dig ni ty (dig´nə ti), **1.** proud and self-respecting manner; stateliness. **2.** way of behaving that wins the respect of others.

dike (dīk), **1.** a bank of earth or a wall

DIKE — WATER — LAND

built as a protection against flooding by a river or the sea. **2.** anything that serves as a dike.

dis as ter (di zas´tər), an event such as a flood, fire, shipwreck, or earthquake, which brings distress to many people; a great misfortune.

dis pute (dis pūt´), disagree with (a statement); declare not true; call in question.

djinn (jin). See **jinn.**

drone (drōn), **1.** male honeybee. **2.** make a deep, continuous, humming sound. **3.** such a sound: *Soldiers*

listened for the drone of the airplane motors. **4.** talk or say in an unchanging voice.

dun der head (dun´dər hed´), a stupid, foolish person.

em bar rass (em bar´əs), make (a person) uneasy; cause to feel shy or uncomfortable (when others are watching or in the company of others): *Meeting strangers embarrassed the shy boy so that he blushed and stammered.*

e merge (i mėrj´), come out; come up; come into view: *The sun emerged from behind a cloud.*

e mer gen cy (i mėr´jən si), sudden need for immediate action: *I keep a flashlight in my car for use in an emergency.*

en vy (en´vi), **1.** discontent because one wishes another's good fortune had been his own: *All the boys were filled with envy when they saw Tom's new bicycle.* **2.** the object of such feeling; person who is envied: *She was the envy of the younger girls in the school.* **3.** feel envy toward.

ev i dent (ev´ə dənt), easy to see or understand; clear; plain: *It is evident that children grow up.*

ex ag ger ate (eg zaj´ər āt), make too large; say or think something is greater than it is; go beyond the truth: *The little boy exaggerated when he said there were thousands of cats in the back yard.*

ex haust (eg zôst´), **1.** to empty: *to exhaust a well.* **2.** to use up: *to exhaust the supply of water, to exhaust one's strength or money.* **3.** tire out: *to exhaust oneself by hard work.*

ex haust ed (eg zôs´tid), **1.** used up. **2.** worn out; very tired.

hat, āge, cãre, fär; let, ēqual, tėrm; it, īce; hot, ōpen, ôrder; oil, out; cup, pút, rüle, ūse; ch, child; ng, long; sh, she; th, thin; ᴛʜ, then; zh, measure; ə represents *a* in about, *e* in taken, *i* in pencil, *o* in lemon, *u* in circus.

ex panse (eks pans′), open or unbroken stretch; a wide, spreading surface: *The Pacific Ocean is a very large expanse of water.*

ex pert (eks′pėrt, also eks pėrt′ for 2), **1.** person who has skill or who knows much about some special thing. **2.** having skill; knowing much about some special thing.

fas ci nate (fas′ə nāt), **1.** charm: *Alice fascinates everyone by her beauty and charm.* **2.** hold motionless by strange power or by terror: *Snakes are said to fascinate small birds.*

fash ion (fash′ən), **1.** to make, shape, or form: *He fashioned a whistle out of a piece of wood.* **2.** the way a thing is shaped or made or done: *He walks in a peculiar fashion.* **3.** style: *She likes to read about the latest fashions.*

feat (fēt), great deed; act requiring great skill, strength, or daring.

flank (flangk), **1.** the side of an animal or a person between the ribs and the hip. **2.** be at the side of: *A garage flanked the house.* **3.** the far right or the far left side of an army, fort, or fleet.

floun der (floun′dər), **1.** plunge about; struggle without making much progress. **2.** be clumsy and make mistakes.

fo cus (fō′kəs), **1.** adjust (a lens, camera, etc.) to make a clear picture. **2.** direct (the mind, a light, etc.) toward one thing: *When studying, he focused his mind on his lessons.*

ford (fôrd), **1.** place where a river, stream, or other body of water is not too deep to cross by walking through the water. **2.** cross (a river, etc.) by walking or driving through the water.

fore man (fôr′mən), man in charge of a group of workmen; man in charge of the work in some part of a factory.

fren zied (fren′zid), frantic; wild; very much excited.

fren zy (fren′zi), brief fury; almost madness; very great excitement.

fun nel (fun′əl), **1.** an open vessel ending at the bottom in a tube. If a funnel is used, anything such as a liquid or grain may be poured into a small opening without spilling. **2.** anything that is shaped like a funnel.

Funnel for pouring

gar ment (gär′mənt), any article of clothing.

gen er al ly (jen′ər əl i), for the most part; usually.

gi gan tic (jī gan′tik), big like a giant; huge.

green horn (grēn′hôrn′), beginner; person who is new at something.

grope (grōp), **1.** feel about with the hands. **2.** find by feeling about with the hands; feel (one's way) slowly: *The blind man groped his way to the door.*

gun ny sack (gun′i sak′), sack or bag made of a strong, coarse material.

hal lo (hə lō′), **1.** call or shout to attract attention. **2.** call of greeting or surprise.

haunch (hônch), the part of the body around the hips: *The dog sat on his haunches.*

haze (hāz), a small amount of mist or smoke in the air: *A haze covered the distant hills.*

heave (hēv), **1.** lift with force or effort: *He heaved the heavy box into the wagon.* **2.** give (a sigh, groan, etc.) with a deep, heavy breath.

hel i cop ter (hel′ə kop′tər), a kind of flying machine.

hey (hā), a sound made to attract attention, express surprise or other feeling, or ask a question: *Hey! stop! Hey? what did you say?*

hob nail (hob′nāl′), short nail with a large head to protect the bottoms of heavy shoes.

Hobnails

ho ri zon (hə rī′zən), the line where earth and sky appear to meet. You cannot see beyond the horizon.

hos tile (hos′təl), 1. of an enemy or enemies: *the hostile army.* 2. unfriendly: *a hostile look.*

hov er (huv′ər), 1. stay in or near one place in the air: *The two birds hovered over their nest.* 2. stay in or near one place: *The dogs hovered around the meat truck.*

hu man (hū′mən), of man; like a man: *Men, women, and children are human beings. Those monkeys look almost human.*

hunch (hunch), 1. draw, bend, or form into a hump: *He sat hunched up with his chin on his knees.* 2. feeling or thought not based on reasoning.

Il li nois (il′ə noi′ or il′ə noiz′), a Middle Western State of the United States.

im ple ment (im′plə mənt), useful article of equipment; tool.

im pres sion (im presh′ən), 1. effect produced on a person: *Punishment seemed to make little impression on the child.* 2. mark or marks made by pressing or stamping: *The thief had left an impression of his foot in the garden.*

im pu dent (im′pū dənt), without shame; forward; rudely bold: *The impudent boy made faces at the stranger.*

in clude (in klüd′), 1. contain: *Their farm includes 160 acres.* 2. put in a total, a class, or the like: *The price includes the land, house, and furniture.*

in cred i ble (in kred′ə bəl), beyond belief; seeming too unusual to be possible: *The soldier fought with incredible courage.*

in spire (in spīr′), put thought, feeling, life, force, etc., into: *The speaker inspired the crowd. John's skill inspired the whole team to play harder.*

jinn (jin), spirits or spirit that can appear in human or animal form and do good or harm to people.

jun ior (jün′yər), 1. the younger (used of a son having the same name as his father). 2. younger person: *Tom is his brother's junior by two years.* 3. of lower position; of less standing than some others: *the junior partner, a junior officer.* 4. of or for younger people.

ker o sene (ker′ə sēn), a thin oil used in lamps and stoves.

knowl edge (nol′ij), 1. what somebody knows: *Tom's knowledge about guns.* 2. act or fact of knowing: *The knowledge of our ball team's success caused great joy.* 3. **To one's knowledge** means as one knows; as far as one knows.

la bor (lā′bər), 1. work; toil. 2. move slowly and heavily.

larch (lärch), a tree with small cones and needles that fall off in the autumn.

Branch of larch

life preserver, a kind of jacket or wide belt, usually made of cloth and cork, to keep a person afloat in the water.

Life preserver

lit ter (lit′ər), **1.** little bits left about in disorder. **2.** scatter things about; leave odds and ends lying around; make untidy: *You have littered the room with your papers.* **3.** the young animals produced at one time: *a litter of puppies.*

lo co (lō′kō), **1.** locoweed. **2.** poison with this weed. **3.** crazy.

loll (lol), **1.** lie, sit, lean, etc., in a lazy manner. **2.** hang loosely: *A dog's tongue lolls out.* **3.** allow to hang loosely: *A dog lolls out his tongue.*

lol lop (lol′əp), go with bounds or leaps; bound or bob up.

lurch (lèrch), **1.** a sudden leaning or roll to one side, like that of a ship, a car, or a staggering person: *The car gave a lurch and upset.* **2.** make a lurch; stagger: *The wounded man lurched forward.*

men ace (men′is), **1.** threat: *In dry weather forest fires are a menace.* **2.** threaten: *Floods menaced the valley towns.*

mer cu ry (mèr′kū ri), a heavy, silver-white metal that is liquid at ordinary temperatures. Mercury is used in thermometers.

mi cro phone (mī′krə fōn), **1.** a device for increasing small sounds. **2.** a radio device for sending out sounds.

mim ic (mim′ik), copy closely: *A parrot can mimic a person's voice.*

Mis sou ri (mə zür′i or mə zür′ə), **1.** large river in the northern part of the United States. **2.** a Middle Western State of the United States.

mourn ful (môrn′fəl), sad; sorrowful.

mud dle (mud′əl), **1.** mix up; bring (things) into a mess: *to muddle a piece of work.* **2.** a mess; disorder; confusion: *When Mother came home, she found the house in a muddle.*

na tion al (nash′ən əl), of a nation; belonging to a whole nation: *national laws, a national disaster.*

nos tril (nos′trəl), either of the two openings in the nose.

nui sance (nü′səns or nū′səns), thing or person that annoys, troubles, or is disagreeable: *Flies are a nuisance.*

nuz zle (nuz′əl), poke or rub with the nose; press the nose against.

of fi cial (ə fish′əl), officer; person holding office: *bank officials.*

O ma ha (ō′mə hô or ō′mə hä), a city in eastern Nebraska.

op pres sive (ə pres′iv), hard to bear; wearying: *The great heat was oppressive.*

Or e gon (ôr′ə gon or ôr′ə gən), a Northwestern State of the United States on the Pacific Coast.

pace (pās), **1.** a step. **2.** to walk with regular steps: *The tiger paced up and down his cage.*

pa lav er (pə lav′ər), **1.** a meeting to discuss something. **2.** flowing talk; smooth, persuading talk. **3.** to talk easily and flatteringly.

Pe cos (pā′kəs).

pelt[1] (pelt), **1.** throw things at; attack. **2.** beat heavily: *The rain came pelting down.*

pelt[2] (pelt), the skin of a sheep, goat, or small fur-bearing animal, before it is tanned.

per il (per′əl), chance of harm; danger: *This bridge is not safe; cross it at your peril.*

Pi erre (pi ãr′).

Platte (plat), a river flowing through Nebraska into the Missouri River.

pli ers (plī′ərz), a tool used to hold or turn or bend things.

Pliers

plight (plīt), condition or state, usually bad: *He was in a sad plight when he became ill and had no money.*

plot (plot), **1.** secret plan: *Two men formed a plot to steal the money.* **2.** to plan; plan secretly with others. **3.** the plan or main events of a story, play, etc.

plough (plou), plow.

plow (plou), **1.** a big heavy tool for cutting the soil and turning it over. **2.** turn up (the soil) with a plow.

pol ish (pol′ish), **1.** make smooth and shiny: *to polish shoes.* **2.** material used to give smoothness or shine.

pomp (pomp), splendid show or display.

pos i tive (poz′ə tiv), admitting of no question or doubt; sure.

pow wow (pou′wou′), a North American Indian word meaning: **1.** a meeting for talk. **2.** hold a powwow.

pre serve (pri zėrv′), keep from harm or change; keep safe; protect.

pro duce (prə düs′ or prə dūs′), bring forward; show: *Produce your proof.*

pro gress (prə gres′ for 1, prog′res for 2), **1.** move forward; go ahead. **2.** an advance; growth; improvement.

prom on to ry (prom′ən tô′ri), a high point of land extending from the coast into the water; headland.

Promontory

pro test (prō′test for 1, prə test′ for 2 and 3), **1.** statement that denies or objects strongly. **2.** declare solemnly. **3.** to object: *The boys protested against having girls in the game.*

pub lish (pub′lish), prepare and offer (a book, paper, map, piece of music, etc.) for sale or distribution.

quar ry[1] (kwôr′i), place where stone is dug, cut, or blasted out for use in building.

quar ry[2] (kwôr′i), animal chased in a hunt; game; prey: *The fox hunters chased their quarry for hours.*

rash[1] (rash), too hasty; careless; taking too much risk: *It is rash to cross the street without looking both ways.*

rash[2] (rash), a breaking out with many small red spots on the skin. Scarlet fever causes a rash.

rear[1] (rēr), **1.** back part; the back: *The kitchen is in the rear of the house.* **2.** back; at the back: *Leave by the rear door of the car.*

rear[2] (rēr), **1.** make grow; help to grow; bring up: *The mother was very careful in rearing her children.* **2.** rise on the hind legs: *The horse reared as the fire engine dashed past.*

re cent (rē′sənt), done or made not long ago: *recent events.*

re cent ly (rē′sənt li), lately; not long ago.

re cord (ri kôrd′ for 1, rek′ərd for 2 and 3), **1.** set down in writing so as to keep for future use: *Listen to the speaker and record what he says.* **2.** the thing written or kept. **3.** the best yet done. **Record time** means time shorter than any time before for the same thing.

---

hat, āge, cãre, fär; let, ēqual, tėrm; it, īce; hot, ōpen, ôrder; oil, out; cup, pùt, rüle, ūse; ch, child; ng, long; sh, she; th, thin; ŦH, then; zh, measure; ə represents *a* in about, *e* in taken, *i* in pencil, *o* in lemon, *u* in circus.

re duce (ri düs′ or ri dūs′),　make less; make smaller: *She is trying to reduce her weight.*

re flect (ri flekt′),　**1.** throw back (light, heat, sound, etc.): *The sidewalks reflect heat on a hot day.* **2.** give back an image of: *The mirror reflects my face.*

re flec tion (ri flek′shən),　something reflected; image: *See the reflection of the tree in this still water.*

reg u lar (reg′ū-lər),　**1.** usual; fixed by custom or rule: *Our regular sleeping place is in a bedroom.* **2.** well-balanced; even in size, spacing, or speed: *regular teeth, regular breathing.*

re hearse (ri hèrs′),　practice for a public performance.

rep u ta tion (rep′ū tā′shən),　**1.** what people think and say the character of a person or thing is. **2.** good name; good reputation. **3.** fame.

re spect (ri spekt′),　high regard: *Children should show respect to those who are older and wiser.*

re tort (ri tôrt′),　**1.** reply quickly or sharply. **2.** a sharp or witty reply.

re view (ri vū′),　**1.** study again; look at again: *Review today's lesson for tomorrow.* **2.** an inspecting: *A review of the troops will be held during the general's visit to camp.*

ri val (rī′vəl),　**1.** person who wants the same thing as another; one who tries to equal or do better than another: *The two boys were rivals for the same class office. They were also rivals in sports.* **2.** wanting the same thing as another; being a rival: *The rival store tried to get the other's trade.* **3.** try to equal or outdo: *The stores rival each other in window displays.* **4.** equal; match: *The sunset rivaled the sunrise in beauty.*

ri val ry (rī′vəl ri),　competition; effort to obtain something another person wants: *There is rivalry among business firms for trade.*

ro de o (rō′di ō or rō dā′ō),　a contest or a show of skill in roping cattle, riding horses, etc.

sap ling (sap′ling),　young tree.

sav age (sav′ij),　**1.** wild: *He likes the savage beauty of the Rocky Mountains.* **2.** fierce; cruel; ready to fight: *The savage lion attacked the hunter.*

scale[1] (skāl),　a balance; a machine for weighing: *She weighed some meat on the scales.* **Tip the scales** means (1) have one's weight. (2) overbalance one for another.

scale[2] (skāl),　size, amount, etc., compared with other sizes, amounts, etc. **On a large scale** or **on a big scale** means in a big way.

sched ule (skej′ül),　**1.** a list. **2.** a written or printed statement showing the time at which things are to be done: *A timetable is a schedule of the coming and going of trains.*

scowl (skoul),　look angry; to frown.

screech (skrēch),　**1.** cry out sharply in a high voice; shriek: *"Help! help!" she screeched.* **2.** a shrill harsh scream: *The woman's screeches brought the police.*

sec tion (sek′shən),　**1.** part cut off; part; division; slice: *Mother cut the pie into eight equal sections.* **2.** a piece of land one mile square.

sel dom (sel′dəm),　rarely; not often: *He is seldom ill.*

se ries (sēr′iz),　**1.** things alike in a row. **2.** things happening one after the other.

se vere (sə vēr′),　**1.** serious: *a severe illness.* **2.** sharp; violent: *I have a severe headache. That was a severe storm.*

shan't (shant),　shall not.

shod (shod). See **shoe**. *The blacksmith shod the horses.*

shoe (shü), **1.** an outer covering for a person's foot. **2.** something used like a shoe: *a horseshoe.* **3.** supply with shoes: *A blacksmith shoes horses.*

shrewd (shrüd), sharp; keen; clever: *He is a shrewd businessman.*

shrink (shringk), **1.** become smaller; make smaller: *Wool shrinks in washing.* **2.** draw back: *The dog shrinks from the whip. She shrinks from meeting strangers.*

sill (sil), piece of wood or stone across the bottom of a door, window, or house frame.

sire (sīr), **1.** male parent. **2.** a title of respect used in the past in speaking to a great noble, and now to a king: *"Your coach, Sire," said the footman.*

skim (skim), **1.** move lightly (over): *The skaters were skimming over the ice.* **2.** glide along: *The swallows went skimming by.*

slab (slab), a broad, flat, thick piece (of stone, wood, meat, etc.).

slack (slak), **1.** not tight or firm; loose: *The rope hung slack.* **2.** part that hangs loose: *He pulled in the slack of the rope.* **3. Slack up** means to slow down or go more slowly.

slack en (slak′ən), **1.** make slower: *Don't slacken your efforts till the work is done.* **2.** make looser: *Slacken the rope.*

sledge ham mer (slej′ ham′ər), a large, heavy hammer.

smith (smith), **1.** man who makes or shapes things out of metal: *a goldsmith, a tinsmith.* **2.** blacksmith.

so ber (sō′bər), quiet; serious; solemn: *John looked sober at the thought of missing the picnic.*

s o d (sod), **1.** ground covered with grass. **2.** piece of this containing the grass and its roots.

sod dy (sod′i), in Western United States, a sod house.

sol i tar y (sol′ə ter′i), **1.** alone; single; only: *A solitary rider was seen in the distance.* **2.** without companions; lonely; away from people: *He leads a solitary life in his hut in the mountains.*

Sol o mon (sol′ə mən), a king of Israel, who was a son of David. He was famous for being wise.

soothe (süŦH), quiet; calm; comfort: *The mother soothed the hurt child.*

spec ta tor (spek′tā tər), person who looks on: *There were many spectators at the game.*

spell bound (spel′bound′), too interested to move; fascinated; enchanted.

spike (spīk), **1.** a large, strong nail. **2.** fasten with spikes.

spin ney (spin′i), thicket.

spur (spėr), **1.** a metal piece worn on a horseman's heel for urging a horse on. **2.** touch with spurs. **3.** anything that urges on. **4.** urge on: *Pride spurred the man to fight.*

Horseman's spur

stam pede (stam pēd′), **1.** a sudden scattering or headlong flight of a frightened herd of cattle or horses. **2.** scatter or flee in a stampede.

stealth y (stel′thi), done in a secret manner; secret; sly.

stir rup (stėr′əp), a support for the rider's foot, hung from a saddle.

Stirrups

---

strain (strān),   **1.** draw tight; stretch: *The weight strained the rope.* **2.** pull hard. **3.** make a very great effort. **4.** press or pour through a strainer: *Strain the soup before serving it.*

stride (strīd),   walk with long steps: *The tall man strides rapidly down the street.*

strode (strōd).   See **stride**. *He strode over the ditch.*

stroll (strōl),   **1.** walk; take a quiet walk for pleasure. **2.** a walk taken without hurry: *We went for a stroll in the park.*

stu di o (stü′di ō or stū′di ō),   **1.** workroom of an artist, person who takes pictures, etc. **2.** place where a radio or television program is given.

sub due (səb dü′ or səb dū′),   soften; tone down: *The window curtains give the room a subdued light.*

suc ces sion (sək sesh′ən),   **1.** the coming of one person or thing after another. **In succession** means one after another. **2.** things happening one after another; a series: *A succession of accidents spoiled our automobile trip.*

suf fer (suf′ər),   have pain, great sadness, etc.: *She suffers from headache.*

sus pi cious (səs pish′əs),   **1.** believing untrue or guilty without proof. **2.** showing doubt.

sway (swā),   **1.** swing back and forth; swing from side to side, or to one side. **2.** make move; cause to sway: *The wind sways the grass.*

swell (swel),   **1.** grow bigger; make bigger. **2.** piece of higher ground; rounded hill.

tai lor (tā′lər),   man whose business is making clothes.

tan (tan),   **1.** make (a hide) into leather by soaking in a special liquid. **2.** yellowish brown: *He wore tan shoes.* **3.** make or become brown by being in sunlight and air: *Sun and wind had tanned the young sailor's face.*

tat too (ta tü′),   make pictures or words on the body by making tiny holes in the skin and putting in colors.

team (tēm),   **1.** number of people working or acting together: *a football team.* **2.** two or more horses or other animals harnessed together to work. **3.** join together in a team.

team ster (tēm′stər),   man whose work is driving a team of horses or hauling things with a truck.

ter race (ter′is),   **1.** a flat, raised piece of land; raised level. **2.** form into a terrace or terraces: *He made a terraced garden.*

Terraces

thick et (thik′it),   bushes or small trees growing close together: *We crawled into the thicket and hid.*

throt tle (throt′əl),   a valve or lever for controlling the supply of steam or gasoline to an engine.

thud (thud),   **1.** a dull sound: *The book hit the floor with a thud.* **2.** hit, move, or strike with a thud.

thus (ᴛʜus),   **1.** in this way: *He spoke thus: "Fourscore and seven years ago."* **2.** therefore: *He studied hard; thus he got high marks.*

tink er (tingk′ər),   **1.** man who mends pots, pans, etc. **2.** work or repair in an unskilled or clumsy way. **3.** to busy oneself with working on or repairing (radios, model trains, or other machines).

tor rent (tôr′ənt),   **1.** a violent, rushing stream of water: *The mountain torrent dashed over the rocks.* **2.** any violent, rushing stream; a flood: *The crazy man poured out a torrent of words.*

trace[1] (trās),   mark left: *We saw traces of rabbits on the snow.*

trace[2] (trās), either of the two strips of leather, ropes, or chains by which an animal pulls a wagon or carriage.

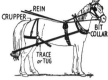

Horse's harness

trans fer (trans fèr′ for 1, trans′fər for 2),   **1.** convey or remove from one person or place to another; hand over: *The old farmer transferred his farm to his son.* **2.** ticket allowing a passenger to continue his journey on another streetcar, bus, or train.

tres pass (tres′pəs),   go on somebody's property without any right: *The farmer put up "No Trespassing" signs to keep people off his farm.*

tri fle (trī′fəl),   **1.** thing having little value or importance. **2.** spend (time, effort, money, etc.) on things having little value: *She had trifled away the whole morning.*

trudge (truj),   **1.** walk. **2.** walk wearily or with effort. **3.** a hard or weary walk: *It was a long trudge up the hill.*

type (tīp),   **1.** a kind, class, or group alike in some important way: *The library has books of many different types.* **2.** piece of metal or wood having on its upper surface a letter for use in printing. **3.** collection of such pieces. **4.** printed letters. **5.** typewrite.

un dis put ed (un′dis pūt′id),   not disputed; not doubted.

un furl (un fèrl′),   spread out; shake out; unfold: *Unfurl the sail.*

un ion (ūn′yən),   joining of two or more persons or things into one: *The United States was formed by the union of thirteen States.*

U tah (ū′tô or ū′tä),   a Western State of the United States.

vac u um (vak′ū əm),   empty space without even air in it.

vacuum cleaner,   machine for cleaning floor coverings, curtains, floors, etc., by suction.

var i ous (vār′i əs),   **1.** different. **2.** several; many.

vault (vôlt),   **1.** to jump or leap over by using the hands or a pole. **2.** to jump; to leap.

ve hi cle (vē′ə kəl),   carriage, cart, wagon, automobile, sled, etc., used on land.

vi cin i ty (və sin′ə ti),   region near or about a place; neighborhood: *No houses in this vicinity are for sale.*

vi sion (vizh′ən),   **1.** power of seeing; sense of sight: *The old man wears glasses because his vision is poor.* **2.** something seen; view. **3.** something seen by imagining, in a dream, etc.: *The poor man had visions of great wealth.*

Wa tam (wô′təm).

wea ri some (wēr′i səm),   wearying; tiring; tiresome.

wea ry (wēr′i),   tired.

weigh (wā),   **1.** find out how heavy a thing is. **2.** have as a measure by weight: *I weigh 110 pounds.*

wil y (wīl′i),   tricky; cunning; crafty; sly: *The wily fox got away.*

yoke (yōk),   **1.** a wooden frame to fasten two work animals together. **2.** harness or fasten a work animal to.

---

hat, āge, cāre, fär;   let, ēqual, tèrm;   it, īce;   hot, ōpen, ôrder;   oil, out;   cup, put, rüle, ūse;   ch, child;   ng, long;   sh, she;   th, thin;   ᴛʜ, then;   zh, measure;   ə represents *a* in about, *e* in taken, *i* in pencil, *o* in lemon, *u* in circus.

TO THE TEACHER

The new *Days and Deeds*, Book 5[1], with its accompanying *Guidebook* and *Think-and-Do Book*, continues The New Basic Reading Program for the middle grades. It is designed for approximately one semester's use whenever the child has successfully completed *More Times and Places*.

The new *Days and Deeds* contains 540 words not introduced by the end of Book 4[2] of The New Basic Reading Program. The majority of these new words are used three or more times in this book. Most of these 540 words will be further repeated in *More Days and Deeds*, Book 5[2] of The New Basic Readers, to insure a minimum of three uses of all new words by the end of Book 5[2].

In the first three units of the new *Days and Deeds*, no page has more than four new words, and no page in the entire book introduces more than five new words. Of the 2742 words introduced in previous New Basic Readers, 98 per cent are repeated in Book 5[1] or Book 5[2].

The 540 new words in this book are shown in the vocabulary list below. The following forms of known words are not counted as new (including those forms made by changing *y* to *i* or *f* to *v*, by dropping the final *e*, or by doubling the final consonant in the root word): forms made by adding or dropping the inflectional endings *s*, *es*, *ed*, *ing*, *n*, *en*, and *er*, *est* of comparison; possessives; forms made by adding or dropping the prefixes *dis-*, *fore-*, *im-*, *re-*, or *un-*, and the suffixes *-en*, *-er*, *-ful*, *-ish*, *-less*, *-ly*, *-ness*, *-or*, *-ward*, or *-teen*, *-th*, or *-ty* of numerals; compounds made up of known words; common contractions. Homographs are not counted as separate words; for example, if *rash* meaning "a breaking out with small red spots on the skin" has been introduced, *rash* meaning "too hasty" is not counted as a separate word. Nonsense words, syllables that represent sounds, and the following foreign words are not counted: *indaba, mochila, punchayet*.

Boys and girls can attack independently all of the 540 new words by applying the word-analysis and dictionary skills developed in The New Basic Reading Program. The words printed in italics in the vocabulary list are those that are included in the glossary of the new *Days and Deeds*.

VOCABULARY LIST

1 deeds	8 lump	16 kids	22 *cushion*
	9 clerk	*protested*	23 *mournfully*
	10 sale	outfit	24 *recently*
	embarrassed	17	chum
Unit I	*challenged*	18 mane	25 proof
	11 *hunch*	19 *deafening*	*strolling*
6 Los Angeles	12 *hey*	20	26 hush
7 modern	13 peaks	21 whisked	*confidently*
project	14	*reared*	27 . . . . .
cherries	15 *foreman's*	fraidy	28 . . . . .
		events	

314

29 Lowell
ridge
Albert
assured
30 . . . . .
31 vest
astride
Solomon
32 *rodeo*
puzzling
clatter
33 fame
celebration
34 *greenhorns*
35 bucked
36 . . . . .
37 amid
emerged
38 Frannie
39 crystal
hike
40 . . . . .
41 depths
shuddered
appealed
42 *shrinking*
chanting
heaving
43 gracious
44 *skimmed*
45 *strode*
46 decorated
47 *benefit*
assistant
48 *produce*
copper
49 . . . . .
50 articles
absolutely
professor
feats
51 sleeves
applause

52 . . . . .
53 date
removed
54 *mercury*
thermometer
drugstore
55 stock
junior
56 *scales*
weighing
Paul
judge
57 hose
curry
evident
58 alleyway
59 *litter*
sprawling
60 crazy
61 . . . . .
62 nervous
63 *reduced*
64 Josie
65 grade
China
Whittier
champions
66 . . . . .
67 . . . . .
68 . . . . .
69 *generally*
reflection
closet
70 umpire
inning
score
spectators
71 . . . . .
72 *frenzied*
dimples
73 . . . . .
74 *absorbed*
responsibility

75 *scowled*
clenched
fist
76 forgive
according
sake
77 . . . . .
78 gasoline
pump
79 *determination*
80 . . . . .
81 . . . . .
82 . . . . .
83 briskly
amount
credit
84 wrist
bless

UNIT II

86 buffalo
Independence
Missouri
savage
87 stout
canvas
implements
88 particularly
French
Pierre
forded
89 shaggy
swell
spurred
90 *stampede*
91 confusion
92 *quarry*
bristled
93 hacked
94 *plight*

95 Nora
eastern
sod
96 chunks
protection
Majors
97 . . . . .
98 stray
wriggle
99 *oats*
horizon
hint
tubs
100 halter
101 gulping
102 Kansas
conversation
103 lasso
vaulting
adjusting
stirrup
104 Jones
Wyoming
Montana
spellbound
105 *exaggerated*
106 *abreast*
107 avoid
detail
droning
relaxed
108 dazed
jolt
wearisome
109 extended
peril
vision
110 incident
111 Flave
Oregon
organ
112 barrel
numb

315

316

317

ILLUSTRATIONS

The pictures in this book were made by Jack White (cover, pp. 1-54, 64-85, 161-171, 184-193, 202-225, 236-259, 273-293); R. J. Bennett (pp. 55-63); Raymon Naylor (pp. 86-94, 102-110, 131-143, 151-160); David G. Wylie (pp. 95-101, 111-130, 144-150); Hank Ford (pp. 172-183, 194-201); George Lopac (pp. 226-235); Earl Blossom (pp. 260-272).

ACKNOWLEDGMENTS

For permission to adapt and use copyrighted material, grateful acknowledgment is made to the following:

To the author for "Which One?" from "Red Roofs and Green Roofs" by Alice Geer Kelsey in *Pictures and Stories;* to Story Parade, Inc. for "Adventure on Lone Gully Trail" from "Adventure on Lone Gulch Trail" by Helen Dickson, copyright, 1944, by Story Parade, Inc., reprinted by permission; to Mr. J. J. McCaleb for "The Echo Mystery" from "The Mysterious Echo" by Jean McCaleb in *Children's Activities;* to the author for "Red Flame" by Nora Burglon in *Children's Play Mate;* to the author for "The Swinging Bridge" by Alletta Jones in *Trails for Juniors;* to the author for "The Silver Penny" by Fletcher D. Slater in *Child Life;* to the author for "Weight for Daniel" by Gertrude Sparks in *Boys Today;* to the author for "A New Star" from "Josie's Home Run" by Ruth G. Plowhead in *Child Life;* to the publishers for "The Big Word" from "Responsibility—A Big Word" by Nan Gilbert, reprinted from *The Instructor*, by permission of F. A. Owen Publishing Company.

To The John C. Winston Company for "Jonathan's Buffalo" by Armstrong Sperry from *Wagons Westward;* to the author for "Homesick Honey" by Miriam Mason Swain; to Charles Scribner's Sons for "Bill Meets a Longhorn" by Phillip A. Rollins from *Jinglebob;* to the publishers for "Pike's Peak or Bust," reprinted by permission of Dodd, Mead & Company from *How They Followed the Golden Trail* by J. Walker McSpadden, copyright, 1941, by Dodd, Mead & Company, Inc.; to the author for "Drums in the Forest" by Fred D. Berkebile in *Boys Today.*

To the author for "The Great Idea" by Ruth Mary Sharp; to the author for "On with the Show" by Ruth Harshaw; to the author and publishers for "Uncle Lem's Egg Beater" from "Hard-Boiled Egg Beater" by Edward C. Janes in *The Open Road for Boys;* to the author for "What's New?" by Eva Nolle; to the author for "All the Difference" by R. O. Work; to the author for "S O S" by Don Stouffer.

To the author and publishers for "Babe, the Blue Ox." Adapted from *Paul Bunyan*, copyright, 1924, and copyright renewed, 1952, by Esther Shephard. Used by permission of Harcourt, Brace and Company, Inc. The language of the original has been materially changed in the adaptation included herein; to Albert Whitman & Co. for "Pecos Bill and the Cyclone" by James C. Bowman from *Pecos Bill;* to the publishers for "The King's Stilts" by Dr. Seuss, copyright, 1939, by Dr. Seuss, reprinted by special permission of Random House, Inc.